Global Loss of Coastal Habitats
Rates, Causes and Consequences

Global Loss of Coastal Habitats
Rates, Causes and Consequences

Edited by
Carlos M. Duarte

Jennifer Culbertson
William C. Dennison
Robinson W. Fulweiler
Terry Hughes
Erin L. Kinney
Núria Marbà
Scott Nixon
Emily E. Peacock
Stephen Smith
Ivan Valiela

Fundación **BBVA**

CATALOGUING-IN-PUBLICATION DATA

Global Loss of Coastal Habitats : Rates, Causes and Consequences / edited by Carlos M. Duarte ; Jennifer Culbertson... [et al.] — 1.ª ed. — Bilbao : Fundación BBVA, 2009.
184 p. ; 18 x 26 cm
ISBN: 978-84-96515-84-0
1. Contaminación de las costas. 2. Deterioro del medio ambiente. I. Duarte, Carlos M. II. Culbertson, Jennifer. III. Fundación BBVA, ed.
574.5

First published, 2009

© the authors, 2009

© of this edition: Fundación BBVA, 2009
Plaza de San Nicolás, 4. 48005 Bilbao

DESIGN AND PRODUCTION:
José Manuel Reyero / Comunicación y Gestión Ambiental ALAIRE, S.L.

EDITOR: Karen Welch

PRINTED BY: V.A. Impresores, S.A.

BOUND BY: Ramos

ISBN: 978-84-96515-84-0
LEGAL DEPOSIT: M-26342-2009

Printed in Spain

The FSC logo (Forest Stewardship Council) means that the virgin fiber used in making this paper has been sourced from forests certified against a set of strict environmental and social standards and controlled sources. Consuming FSC paper is a way to support the sustainable use and conservation of the world's forests.

CONTENTS

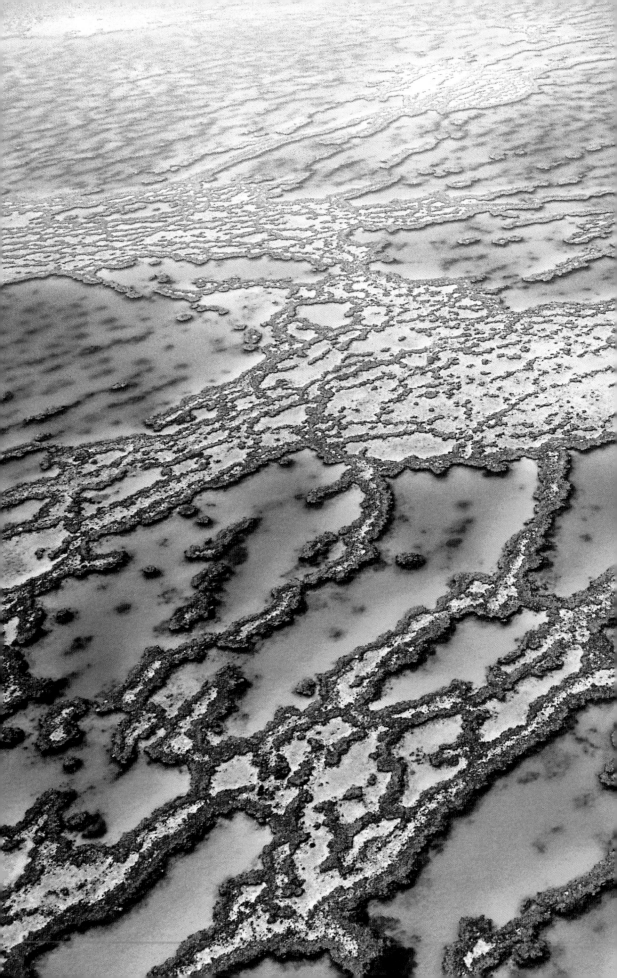

INTRODUCTION

Carlos M. Duarte
Mediterranean Institute for Advanced Studies (IMEDEA)
Spanish National Research Council (CSIC)-University of the Balearic Islands (UIB)
Esporles, Mallorca, Spain

THE ECOSYSTEMS PRESENT in boundaries between biomes typically rank amongst the most productive and diverse on the planet (McClain et al. 2003). The coastline, with about 300,000 to 1,000,000 km of length globally, represents the boundary between the two largest domains for life on Earth, the land and the oceans, and is home to highly productive and diverse ecosystems. In particular, marine coastal habitats include salt marshes, mangrove forests, coral reefs, seagrass meadows and algal beds that once occupied much of the global coastline, extending as a belt along the coastline from the bottom of the photic layer, the depth receiving sufficient light to allow the growth of marine primary producers, to the upper limit of the intertidal zone. Analysis of the irradiance fields of the coastal ocean has revealed that the area able to support these coastal habitats occupies about 30% of the global shelf (Gattuso et al. 2006). Coral reefs and mangrove forests are generally confined to tropical and subtropical coasts, with minimum seawater temperatures of about 20°C, although mangroves occur in colder waters along the coast of Asia (e.g., northern Vietnam). Seagrass meadows occur across a broad latitudinal range and are only absent from Antarctica, while macroalgal beds are found on every coastline. Salt marshes occur on temperate coastlines, particularly those with a significant tidal range. Salt marshes and mangroves occupy the upper intertidal area, whereas seagrass and macroalgal beds extend from the subtidal to the lower intertidal and coral reefs grow in the subtidal zone.

Coastal habitats rank amongst the most productive in the world, with overall rates of primary production comparable to those of the rainforest (Cebrián and Duarte 1996). They are also important biodiversity hotspots supporting rich species assemblages. This renders them important habitats for biodiversity conservation, as they frequently harbor endangered species. Although coral reefs are credited with being oceanic analogs to the tropical forest, for the biodiversity they support, recent analyses have shown that other, less charismatic

◄ **Photo 1: Mangrove forest, Borneo.** Mangrove forests are highly productive ecosystems, rich in biodiversity, found along river deltas on tropical coasts.

Photo 2: *Cymodocea* meadows, Canary Islands. This fast-growing angiosperm, which advances along the seabed at a rate of several meters per year, forms highly productive ecosystems along the Atlantic and Mediterranean coasts.

coastal habitats, among them seagrass meadows, also shelter a wide range of endangered and threatened marine species, such as seahorses or dugongs, which outnumber seagrass species by a factor of 10 (Hughes et al. 2008). Hence conserving coastal habitats is a sound strategy for the conservation of many threatened marine species. In addition to their resident fauna, they serve as nursery grounds for numerous species that recruit in these habitats before going off to live their adult lives elsewhere. Many of these species are commercially important, so the rich biodiversity characteristic of coastal habitats is also a source of food for human populations around the world.

The high production of coastal areas also renders them important sites for carbon sequestration. Vegetated coastal habitats, particularly salt marshes, seagrass meadows, and mangrove forests, have recently been shown to sequester 111 Tg C year^{-1} in their sediments (Duarte, Middelburg, and Caraco 2005). This represents 50% of all carbon sequestration in ocean sediments, by habitats that together cover less than 2% of the ocean surface (Duarte, Middelburg, and Caraco 2005). Indeed coastal habitats contribute to stabilize sediments in the presence of wave energy. In addition, the complex canopies and structures they develop and the reef structures they form help to dissipate wave energy and shelter the shoreline from physical disturbances; a major, though largely unrecognized service that coastal habitats provide to society. Because of these and other important functions, such as nutrient cycling—likewise a product of their high production and metabolic rates—coastal habitats are acknowledged as ranking among the most valuable ecosystems on Earth. Coral reefs, mangrove forests, salt marshes, and seagrass meadows have been estimated to deliver the highest value, in terms of ecosystem services (US\$[1992]6,000–19,000 ha^{-1}), of all natural ecosystems on the planet (Costanza et al. 1997). In comparison, the services provided by tropical forests were estimated to supply US\$(1997)2,000 ha^{-1}.

The services society receives from ecosystems have become increasingly compromised, with human population growth and the associated pressures on the environment leading to the worldwide decline of key ecosystems, eroding biological diversity and ecosystem functions (e.g., Balmford, and Bond 2005). This is especially apparent in the coastal zone that is home to a large part of the global human population, of which 37% lives within just 100 km of the coastline. This proportion is growing, moreover, as a result of population growth and migration to these regions, with the result that seventy per cent of the world's megacities (> 1.6 million) are now located on the coastal strip (LOICZ 2002).

Photo 3: Coral reefs. These formations sustain a high biomass and a vast diversity of fish, especially in their unexploited state.

The ensuing anthropogenic pressures on coastal habitats have led to a sustained global loss of coral reefs, mangrove forests, salt marshes, and seagrass meadows over the past five decades. The global loss rate of threatened coastal ecosystems is estimated at 4-9% yr^{-1} for corals, a minimum of 1-2% yr^{-1} for salt marshes, 1-3% yr^{-1} for mangrove forests, and 2-5% yr^{-1} for seagrass meadows (Duarte et al. 2008), all of which exceed the global loss rate of tropical forests, estimated at 0.5% yr^{-1} (Achard et al. 2002). The drivers of these losses are multiple, including land reclamation, coastal development, excess sediment, nutrient and organic inputs—with the resulting spread of coastal hypoxia (Vaquer-Sunyer and Duarte 2008)—overfishing, mechanical damage by boats and fishing gear, logging, impacts from invasive species and intensive aquaculture, and the influence of climate change. These pressures do not act in isolation and, rather than delivering additive impacts, involve feedback processes and synergies that multiply their individual effects on coastal ecosystems.

The impacts of losses of coastal habitats are far reaching, since they not only erode biodiversity, but also reduce the provision of the valuable ecosystem functions associated with coastal ecosystems. The importance of these services can best be understood by reference to a key, but largely unrecognized function; the protection of coastal communities from natural disasters. This was dramatically illustrated in December 2004 when the large tsunami that struck Southeast Asia caused a much higher death toll in coastal villages devoid of mangrove protection than in those with preserved pockets of mangroves (Kathiresan and Rajendran 2005). It is also now recognized that the damage wreaked by Hurricane Katrina (August 2005) was exacerbated by the extensive loss of salt marshes in the Mississippi River delta (Tibbetts 2006).

One response to these events has been an effort to increase our understanding of the role of coastal habitats in delivering services to society, and of the causes and consequences of their loss. It is vital, however, that this understanding is accompanied by greater public awareness of the nature and dimension of the problem, in order to promote effective management and protect or restore the ecosystems under threat. Yet an analysis of publication effort and public awareness, as measured by news reports and stories in the worldwide media, reveals that the level of awareness is not correlated with the scientific effort, and that some habitats, particularly seagrass meadows, receive disproportionately less attention than more popular systems like coral reefs or tropical forests (Duarte et al. 2008). Indeed seagrass meadows tend to lack charisma and have been labeled the "ugly ducklings" of conservation efforts (Duarte et al. 2008). However the fact that even the "higher-

Photo 4: Coral reefs come in a variety of shapes and colors. They receive their coloration from the pigments of symbiotic algae living within their tissues.

profile" habitats, such as coral reefs, are still registering substantial losses shows how far away we are from engaging effective conservation support. Large-scale restoration efforts are possible for some coastal habitats, as demonstrated by the Vietnamese people's afforestation of the large mangrove forest of the Mekong Delta, following its mass destruction by the defoliating Agent Orange used by the U.S. Air Force during the Vietnam War (Stellman et al. 2003). But, aside from small-scale demonstration projects, the recovery of other coastal habitats, particularly seagrass meadows and coral reefs, may involve timescales ranging from decades to millennia. Hence a conservative approach to the management of coastal habitats, emphasizing the prevention of losses, must prevail over approaches based on the perspective of compensatory actions to restore damaged ecosystems.

This volume seeks to increase awareness of the loss of coastal habitats by providing detailed analyses, global in scope, of the scale of such losses and their causes and consequences for individual systems. Hence chapters are devoted to changes in the seagrass habitat at a global scale (Dennison) and in the Mediterranean Sea (Marbà), losses in salt marsh and mangrove ecosystems (Valiela et al.), and those affecting coral reefs (Hughes). Room is also found for a detailed analysis of the eutrophication of the coastal ocean (Nixon and Fulweiler), a major driver of the deterioration and subsequent loss of coastal habitats. Its origins lie in the talks delivered at the BBVA Foundation–Cap Salines Lighthouse Coastal Research Station Colloquium held in Madrid on October 10, 2007, which also lends its title to the present volume. This Colloquium was the third in a series addressing issues in marine ecology and biodiversity, with previous editions dedicated to scientific and technological challenges in the exploration of marine biodiversity and the impacts of climate warming on polar ecosystems respectively. Colloquium presentations can be viewed in full on the BBVA Foundation website[1], which provides a useful complement, particularly for teaching purposes, to the chapters of this book.

The reviews undertaken in these chapters converge to demonstrate high loss rates of coastal habitats, driven by the rapid occupation of the coastline by humans, increased inputs of nutrients to coastal ecosystems, and the emerging impacts of climate change. While the occupation of the coastline by infrastructures and eutrophication are processes unfolding locally, their occurrence is sufficiently widespread as to constitute a global phenomenon. Climate change, which comes on top of these pressures to deliver the *coup de grâce* to already

---

[1] http://www.fbbva.es/TLFU/tlfu/ing/areas/medioamb/conferencias/fichaconfe/index.jsp?codigo=653

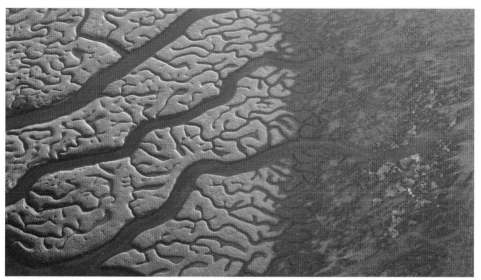

Photo 5: Salt marshes. These habitats have a complex drainage structure with plant life differentiated into levels, from angiosperms at the upper tidal limit to clumps of seaweed at the bottom.

stressed coastal habitats, operates through three main forces: warming, affecting the physiological processes and life-history patterns of marine species; sea level rise, with the associated coastal erosion; and the increase in CO_2 concentration, causing the acidification of seawater, which may enhance photosynthetic rates but at the same time impact negatively on calcifying organisms. One important thread running through the book is the evidence that the impacts of climate change are not gradual and incremental. Rather there are thresholds of climate forcing beyond which impacts on organisms and ecosystems increase abruptly, in some cases threatening catastrophic mortality, as has been demonstrated for coral reefs (Hughes) and seagrass meadows (Marbà). There is, therefore, a need to manage these risks conservatively, in the knowledge that we cannot afford to cross those thresholds, with the loss of biodiversity and valuable ecosystem services that would certainly ensue. I trust that the chapters presented in this book will provide a useful departure point for those eager to learn about the scale of the threats facing coastal habitats, and for those whose job it is to manage and conserve them.

ACKNOWLEDGEMENTS

We thank the BBVA Foundation for their support for the Colloquium from which this book stems, as well as its careful and professional editing. We thank

Cathrin Scupin, Karen Welch and Jose Manuel Reyero, and the staff at FBBVA and Alaire Ediciones, for their help in assembling this volume.

REFERENCES

ACHARD, F., H. D. EVA, H. J. STIBIG, P. MAYAUX, J. GALLEGO, T. RICHARDS, and J. P. MAL-INGREAU. "Determination of Deforestation Rates of the World's Humid Tropical Forests." *Science* 297 (2002): 999-1002.

BALMFORD A., and W. BOND. "Trends in the state of nature and their implications for human well-being." *Ecology Letters* 8 (2005): 1218-1234.

COSTANZA, R., R. D'ARGE, R. DE GROOT, S. FARBER, M. GRASSO, B. HANNON, K. LIM-BURG, et al. "The value of the world's ecosystem services and natural capital." *Nature* 387 (1997): 253-60.

DUARTE, C. M., J. MIDDELBURG, and N. CARACO. "Major role of marine vegetation on the oceanic carbon cycle." *Biogeosciences* 2 (2005): 1-8.

DUARTE, C. M., and J. CEBRIÁN. "The fate of marine autotrophic production." *Limnology and Oceanography* 41 (1996): 1758-1766.

DUARTE, C. M., W. C. DENNISON, R. J. W. ORTH, and T. J. B. CARRUTHERS. "The charisma of coastal ecosystems: addressing the imbalance." *Estuaries and Coasts* 31 (2008):233–238.

GATTUSO, J.-P., B. GENTILI, C. M. DUARTE, J. A. KLEYPAS, J. J. MIDDELBURG, and D. ANTOINE. "Light Availability in the Coastal Ocean: Impact on the Distribution of Benthic Photosynthetic Organisms and their Contribution to Primary Production." *Biogeosciences* 3 (2006): 489-513.

HUGHES, R. A., S. L. WILLIAMS, C. M. DUARTE, K. L. HECK, JR., and M. WAYCOTT. "Associations of concern: Declining seagrasses and threatened dependent species." *Frontiers in Ecology and the Environment* 7, doi:10.1890/080041.

KATHIRESAN, K., and N. RAJENDRAN. "Coastal mangrove forests mitigated tsunami." *Estuarine, Coastal and Shelf Science* 65 (2005): 601-606.

LOICZ (Land Ocean Interaction in the Coastal Zone). *Report of the LOICZ synthesis and futures meeting 2002: coastal change and the anthropocene.* LOICZ International Project Office (IPO), Netherlands Institute for Sea Research (NIOZ), Texel, The Netherlands.

MCCLAIN M. E., E. W. BOYER, C. L. DENT, S. E. GERGEL, N. B. GRIMM, P. M. GROFF-MAN, S. C. HART et al. "Biogeochemical hotspots and hot moments at the interface of terrestrial and aquatic ecosystems." *Ecosystems* 6 (2003): 301-312.

STELLMAN J., S. STELLMAN, R. CHRISTIAN, T. WEBER, and C. TOMASALLO. "The extent and patterns of usage of Agent Orange and other herbicides in Vietnam." *Nature* 422 (2003): 681-687

TIBBETTS, J. "Louisiana's Wetlands: A Lesson in Nature Appreciation." *Environmental Health Perspectives* 114A (2006): 40–43.

VAQUER-SUNYER, R., and C. M. DUARTE. "Thresholds of hypoxia for marine biodiversity." *Proceedings of the National Academy of Sciences* 105 (2008): 15452–15457.

1. NUTRIENT POLLUTION, EUTROPHICATION, AND THE DEGRADATION OF COASTAL MARINE ECOSYSTEMS

Scott W. Nixon[1] and Robinson W. Fulweiler[2]
[1] Graduate School of Oceanography, University of Rhode Island,
Narragansett, RI, United States
[2] Department of Earth Sciences, Boston University,
Boston, MA, United States

1.1. INTRODUCTION

IF A COASTAL MARINE ECOLOGIST had been asked a century ago what the most dangerous things that people put into the sea were, he would probably have settled on the various types of contagion that made people sick with typhoid, cholera, and dysentery. Floating filth, such as the remains of carcasses from slaughterhouses, might also have made his list. Fifty years ago the same question might have generated answers implicating oil, heavy metals, pesticides, and vast quantities of organic matter (largely from human sewage) that consumed much of the oxygen in tidal rivers and estuaries. Thanks to great advances in sanitary engineering, enhanced environmental consciousness and enormous investments in sewage treatment infrastructure in many parts of the world, today's marine ecologist would almost certainly have a very different set of things on her list. The three most dangerous things that we put into the sea today may well be fresh water, fishing nets, and nutrients.

While sea level rise from melting glaciers and overfishing from greed and inept management are clearly great threats to coastal marine ecosystems around the world, our purpose in this chapter is to focus on nutrients, especially nitrogen, and their link to eutrophication. Nutrient pollution is perhaps less widely recognized as a threat to coastal marine ecosystems than sea level rise or overfishing, but the issue began receiving a lot of political attention in much of northwestern Europe some thirty years ago (deJong 2006). There is continuing attention to the problem among coastal managers in the United States (e.g., Bricker et al. 2007), Europe (e.g., Ærtebjerg, Andersen, and Hansen 2003; Langmead and McQuatters-Gollop 2007), and internationally (e.g., UNEP and WHRC 2007; SCOPE 2007; Selman 2007; INI 2007).

◀ **Photo 1.1: Coral reefs are among the most nutrient sensitive coastal marine ecosystems.** This reef formation lies in the crystal clear waters of the Red Sea off Ras Mohammed, Egypt.

1.1.1. Some definitions

In spite of an effort to provide a simple operational definition of eutrophication over a decade ago (Nixon 1995), the term is still used in fuzzy and often confusing ways by scientists and managers alike. To some, the term means high concentrations of nutrients (usually nitrogen, N and/or phosphorus, P), or high inputs of nutrients, or low concentrations of dissolved oxygen, or high concentrations of chlorophyll, or large amounts of algae or dead fish on beaches, or foul smelling air. But eutrophication is actually much more interesting and important:

– *Eutrophication* (noun)—an increase in the rate of supply of organic matter to an ecosystem.

This definition emphasizes that eutrophication is a *process*, a change, an increase in the organic carbon (C) and energy available to the ecosystem—it is not a condition. Some confusion arises because ecologists use the term "eutrophic" to characterize systems that have high primary production (the rate of carbon fixation or formation of new organic matter from carbon dioxide and nutrients). All of the conditions listed above may be found in coastal marine ecosystems that are eutrophic, but they are not necessarily indicators of eutrophication. There is no universally accepted standard for the level of production that must be present for a marine ecosystem to be considered eutrophic. One frequently used guideline is 300 to 500 g C m^{-2} y^{-1} (Nixon 1995). There is a possibility that some marine waters may always have been eutrophic, including upwelling areas off the coast of Peru and parts of Africa. Many others have become eutrophic because of eutrophication brought on by human actions. For example, some parts of the Baltic may be undergoing eutrophication as their primary production rises from 20 to 40 g C m^{-2} y^{-1}, but they are not yet eutrophic. By the same token, an estuary with relatively stable average production of 350 g C m^{-2} y^{-1} may be eutrophic, but it is not experiencing eutrophication.

When defined as above, there are two types of marine eutrophication that are closely related but different in some important ways. Unfortunately, the terms ecologists use to refer to them are awkward:

– *Allocthonous eutrophication*—when the increasing supply of organic matter to the ecosystem comes from outside the system.

– *Autochthonous eutrophication*—when the increasing supply of organic matter comes from increasing primary production within the system.

1.1.2. Organic loading from sewage and industrial wastes

The first great wave of coastal marine eutrophication was allocthonous and occurred in urban coastal areas beginning in the second half of the nineteenth century as public water supplies and then sewer systems were installed in wealthier cities in Europe and North America (e.g., Tarr 1971, 1996; Wood 1982; Nixon 1995; Melosi 2000; Nixon et al. 2008). Large amounts of organic matter from some forms of industry (e.g., food processing, paper, textiles) and human sewage were collected and efficiently carried to rivers draining to the sea or discharged directly in bays and estuaries. Public health impacts, such as the consequences of drinking contaminated water and eating contaminated shell fish, and obvious aesthetic considerations quickly made it apparent that some form of treatment was needed. For the most part, this consisted of screening, settling, and chlorination in the primary treatment of sewage. While this was largely effective in protecting human health and sensibilities, it did little to reduce the organic loading to coastal waters, and oxygen conditions in many urban estuaries deteriorated dramatically. The low (hypoxic) and complete absence of dissolved oxygen (anoxic) conditions began to reduce the abundance and diversity of bottom animals, block anadromous fish migra-

Photo 1.2: Sewage effluent. The plumbing of cities to supply water for drinking and fire protection and to remove water from sewage, industrial waste, and storm water runoff made it easy to transfer nutrients from the land to coastal waters.

tions, produce fish kills, and stimulate the production of noxious hydrogen sulfide gas that occasionally blackened the lead-based paint on waterfront houses. In temperate areas, many of the ecological impacts of increasing the supply of organic matter from land to coastal waters were thoroughly studied and documented during the 1950s to 1970s (e.g., review by Cronin 1967; McIntyre 1977; Pearson and Rosenberg 1978; Warwick and Clarke 1994). In many cases, a dramatic reduction in organic loading to estuaries did not come until the environmental movement of the 1960s and 1970s brought full secondary sewage treatment to the cities of the developed nations. Secondary treatment reduces markedly the biological oxygen demand or BOD of sewage effluent. The untreated discharge of large amounts of organic matter in sewage remains a problem in many developing countries, even where primary chlorination protects human health.

1.1.3. Nutrient enrichment

Autochthonous eutrophication emerged as a serious concern in the coastal marine environment much more recently (Nixon 1995). By far the most common cause of this type of eutrophication is anthropogenic enrichment with the fertilizing nutrients N and P. In some ways it is surprising that these were not widely recognized as potentially important pollutants of coastal marine ecosystems until the late 1960s and 1970s (Wulff 1990; Nixon 1995 and in press; Howarth and Marino 2006). While limnologists were ahead of marine ecologists in recognizing the impact of nutrient enrichment (e.g., National Academy of Sciences 1969), the central role of P in lake eutrophication was also not fixed conclusively until the 1970s (reviewed by Schindler 2006).

Although nutrient enrichment is by far the most common cause of coastal marine and freshwater autochthonous eutrophication, it is useful to note that it is not the only cause. Other changes can also increase the supply of organic matter from primary production within a bay or estuary (e.g., Cloern 2001; Caraco, Cole, and Strayer 2006). For example, dams constructed in the watershed commonly reduce the transport of suspended sediment downstream to an estuary. This can increase the clarity of the water in a previously turbid estuary and thus increase primary production. If chemicals toxic to marine phytoplankton are removed by waste water treatment (for example copper by industrial pre-treatment), primary production might increase. Filling across the mouth of an estuary or lagoon for road construction might increase the water residence time in the system and thus increase production. Human (or other) predators might consume filter feeding shell fish or prey on zooplankton that graze on phytoplankton, and thus increase primary production. And large-scale changes in climate and/or hydrography may act to increase production in complex ways that are not yet fully understood: for example, the recent increases in the abundance of phytoplankton in the North Sea and northeast Atlantic (Richardson and Schoeman 2004; McQuatters-Gollop et al. 2007).

Such interesting exceptions aside, there is no question that anthropogenic nutrient enrichment is responsible for the vast majority of coastal ecosystems experiencing eutrophication, now or in future. And it is clear that nutrient-driven coastal eutrophication has been increasing dramatically in recent decades. Ivan Valiela summarized it well in his excellent new book on global coastal change (Valiela 2006): "Even within the limitations of available infor-mation, it was evident that [coastal marine] eutrophication was widespread, and increasing, into the 21st century." Autochthonous eutrophication from nutrient fertilization is much more widespread and damaging than that caused by organic loading. It is not restricted to coastal waters surrounding large urban or industrial areas and, once added to an ecosystem, N and P can be recycled many times. In other words, the inorganic N or P added to the sys-tem stimulates the production of organic matter by plants. As this organic matter dies and decomposes, it consumes dissolved oxygen. However, the decomposition also releases the N and P which can then be used again by plants to fix yet more organic matter. This recycling may occur many times before an atom of N or P is flushed from an estuary.

Of course, the organic matter added to rivers and estuaries by sewage treat-ment plants also contained N and P, so the early allocthonous eutrophication also produced local autochthonous eutrophication. In reading the historical literature, it is clear that this complication was little appreciated by urban san-itarians or marine biologists—the much more dramatic and visible local impacts of massive organic loading largely overshadowed nutrient enrich-ment. If nutrient enrichment had been considered at all during the late 1800s and the first half of the 1900s, it would almost certainly been seen in a positive light as stimulating natural productivity along the coast (Johnstone 1908; Nixon and Buckley 2002; Nixon, in press).

The first implication of inorganic nutrients as an anthropogenic pollutant with negative impacts in the coastal marine environment appears to have been a result of the studies of phytoplankton blooms ("green tides") conducted by John Ryther (1954, 1989) in Great South Bay and Moriches Bay on Long Island, New York. This work identified nitrogen enrichment from duck farms as the probable cause of the blooms and set the stage for a later paper that would have a much greater impact. The publication in 1971 of "Nitrogen, phosphorus, and eutrophication in the coastal marine environment" by Ryther and Dunstan in *Science* magazine clearly focused the attention of the marine research community on inorganic N as the nutrient whose supply most commonly limited the growth of phytoplankton in coastal waters. This set marine eutrophication apart from the more established paradigm of P limitation in lakes, and stimulated decades of research and management focused on N in coastal areas. In truth, however, the Ryther and Dunstan (1971) paper was the rediscovery of a view established seventy years earlier by the work of marine scientists in Europe. As Mills (1989) noted in his outstanding history of biological oceanography: "The history of [marine] plankton dynamics after 1899 is largely the history of the nitrogen cycle." While the role of N as the most common and pervasive limiting nutrient in temperate marine coastal waters has been confirmed repeatedly in bioassays, mesocosm experiments, numerical models, and stoichiometric analyses, it has also become clear that P limitation may be important in some parts of some estuaries, especially during times of high freshwater inflow (Howarth and Marino 2006). It is also clear that P limitation may be more common in tropical systems with carbonate sediments that can bind tightly with P (e.g., Nielsen, Koch, and Madden 2007). Because of the well recognized importance of N pollution in contributing to the eutrophication of most temperate (and many tropical) coastal ecosystems, most of this discussion will focus on N, including its sources, its pathways of entry to the coastal marine environment, and its effects. These are all topics that have received a great deal of attention in the scientific literature and in the popular press in recent decades. Scientific compilations include special issues of the journals *Estuaries* (Rabalais and Nixon 2002), *Ambio* (Galloway and Cowling 2002), *Limnology and Oceanography* (Smith, Joy, and Howarth 2006), and *Ecological Applications* (Kennish and Townsend 2007). Good non-technical overviews are given in two brief "white papers" from the Ecological Society of America (Vitousek et al. 1997 and Howarth et al. 2000), and in more extended form in *Global Coastal Change* (Valiela 2006).

1.2. NITROGEN AND EUTROPHICATION IN COASTAL MARINE SYSTEMS

Nitrogen pollution has a number of consequences in coastal marine ecosystems, in addition to stimulating an increase in the amount of organic matter being produced. Among some of the more thoroughly documented is chang-

Photo 1.3: Adult of the endangered green sea turtle (*Chelonia mydas*), a species which grazes on seagrass. These grasses do not survive in nutrient enriched waters, where they are shaded out by phytoplankton blooms.

ing the type and species of plants that make the organic matter. This may take the form of subtle shifts in the species composition of phytoplankton (e.g., Turner 2002) or more conspicuous changes in the types of plants supporting the ecosystem. Changes in the species and size composition of the phytoplankton can have important implications for the grazing animals in the water column and on the bottom that feed on them (e.g., Olsen et al. 2006; Wolowicz et al. 2006). It is also possible that nutrient enrichment and eutrophication are contributing to the reported increases in harmful algal blooms around the world, but this linkage remains more controversial. As concluded by Anderson et al. (2002) after an extensive review, "… the relationships between nutrient delivery and the development of blooms and their potential toxicity or harmfulness remains poorly understood … Nutrient enrichment has been strongly linked to stimulation of some harmful species, but for others it has not been an apparent contributing factor."

It has become increasingly clear that N fertilization of shallow low nutrient waters where rooted seagrasses dominate can increase the fouling of the seagrass leaves by epiphytes, produce dense floating mats of drift macroalgae, and ultimately result in intense blooms of phytoplankton. All of these conspire to shade the seagrass to such an extent that it may be completely eliminated even at very low levels of nutrient enrichment (e.g., Twilley et al. 1985; Duarte 1995; Corredor et al. 1999; Nixon et al. 2001; Valiela 2006). There is also some experimental evidence from mesocosms that the impact of nitrogen on temperate coastal lagoons with eelgrass (*Zostera marina*) is exacerbated by even small increases in temperature (Bintz et al. 2003). Studies by Deegan (2002) have also shown that the habitat value of seagrass beds for fish may be seriously reduced by nutrient enrichment, well before the grasses are completely eliminated.

Coral reefs appear to be even more sensitive to nutrient enrichment than seagrass meadows (D'Elia 1988) and have been described as "… the most nutrient-sensitive of all ecosystems." (Goreau 2003). Perhaps the best documented demonstration of the impacts of nutrient enrichment on coral reefs comes from the detailed study of reef recovery in Kaneohe Bay, Hawaii following the diversion of sewage effluents (Smith et al. 1981; Nixon et al. 1986). Unfortunately, continued population growth in the Kaneohe Bay watershed and in non-point sources of N to the system appear to have reversed some of the recovery, and macroalgal overgrowth is once again a problem on the reefs (e.g., Stimson, Larned, and McDermid 1996). Coral reefs represent a case in which nutrient enrichment may cause dramatic species changes, habitat structural changes, and increased organic production simultaneously, as soft or fleshy macroalgae overgrow hard encrusting algae and coral. However, given the high complexity and great diversity of coral reefs, it is perhaps not surprising that the role of nutrient enrichment in coral reef degradation remains controversial within the scientific community (e.g., Lapointe 1997; Hughes et al. 1999; and Lapointe 1999). A recent review concluded that evidence for nutrient enrichment being a major cause of the world-wide degradation of coral reefs was "… equivocal at best." (Szmant 2002). The situation is complicated by the common co-occurrence of overfishing and nutrient enrichment, and some investigators have argued that the overharvesting of herbivorous fish and/or the loss of grazers (e.g., sea urchins) to disease have been more important than anthropogenic nutrient fertilization in promoting macroalgal overgrowth (Szmant 2002). In fact, a recent review has argued that many of the negative changes attributed to nutrient enrichment in seagrass, rocky intertidal, and coral reef communities are really due to human alterations of coastal food webs (Heck and Valentine 2007). On the other hand, several of the major studies supporting the importance of "top-down" or grazing effects on macroalgae on reefs have been vigorously criticized (Goreau 2003), and it seems compelling that nutrient enrichment can play an important role in local reef degradation. On a larger scale, storm damage, coral diseases, warming, and sedimentation must also be important factors (Rogers and Miller 2006).

Regardless of their obvious importance, these various responses to nitrogen enrichment are not, in themselves, eutrophication (with the possible exception of increases in net ecosystem production due to macroalgal growth on coral reefs). They are responses to nutrient enrichment, certainly, but they may or may not be associated with an increase in the production of organic matter in the system. When eutrophication does occur, it may be associated with these or other changes, some of which may be seen as desirable and others not. Among the desirable changes in phytoplankton-based systems may be an increase in benthic animals and the production of harvestable fish, at least up to some point at which hypoxia or anoxia may outweigh the positive influence of a greater food supply (Nixon 1988; Caddy 1993; Herman et al. 1999; Breitburg 2002; Nixon and Buckley 2002; Kemp et al. 2005; Oczkowski and Nixon 2008). And it is the occurrence of hypoxia and anoxia that is the best documented and understood and, perhaps, most severe impact of eutrophication (e.g., Diaz and Rosenberg 2001; Rabalais and Turner 2001). It is the link between N (or, in some cases, P) inputs and accelerated organic production and resulting low oxygen that is the most common concern for managers and marine ecologists. It is this threat that unifies allocthonous and autochthonous eutrophication and thus makes much of the research from earlier decades a helpful platform for understanding what may be the most widespread impact of nutrient pollution.

1.2.1. The oxygen problem

If you are not a limnologist or an oceanographer, you may find yourself puzzled by why we worry about fertilizing lakes and bays with nutrients and making the plants grow faster. And why more plants may mean less oxygen. After all, farmers and gardeners use nutrients to accelerate plant growth all the time on land. And there are popular bumper stickers asking if one has thanked a green plant lately—presumably for making oxygen for us to breathe. The reasons have to do with important differences between air and water. First, a cubic meter of air contains about 270 g of oxygen, while the same volume of sea water in equilibrium with the air only holds 5-10 g of oxygen, depending on its salinity and temperature (warmer and/or saltier holds less oxygen). But much more important is the fact that it takes very little energy to mix air—no one worries about having to keep moving to avoid consuming all the oxygen in the air in front of their face! Water is more viscous and it requires much more mechanical energy to provide turbulent mixing in water than in air. As a result it is quite possible for local oxygen to become depleted when winds or currents are not active. This is taken to an extreme when aquatic systems become vertically stratified in response to solar warming and/or freshwater inflows. Since estuaries are by definition semi-enclosed places where the salinity is diluted by fresh water (Pritchard 1967), they are susceptible to both agents of stratification. Solar energy warms the surface waters and thus makes them less dense than the cooler water below. Fresh water is less dense than salty water and tends to float on the surface. The greater the density difference between the warmer fresher surface water and the cooler saltier bottom water, the more wind and tidal energy is needed to mix them. When the water is strongly stratified, the deeper water may not come into contact with the air for many days or even months. As respiration of organisms in the deeper water and in the bottom sediments proceeds, especially at the higher rates that come with higher summer temperatures, the oxygen in the bottom water becomes more and more depleted. Once it is completely consumed and the water and sediments are anoxic, toxic hydrogen sulfide is produced. In this way even some organisms that can tolerate low or even no oxygen conditions for short times may be killed. While mobile animals like fish can usually avoid hypoxic and anoxic areas, they sometimes become trapped against the shore and cannot escape. In some other situations, wind and tidal mixing may be so weak and respiration rates so high that even the surface waters can become hypoxic or (rarely) anoxic and cause fish kills.

Conspicuous blooms of macroalgae and phytoplankton that may result from nutrient enrichment do produce oxygen as land plants do, but this takes place only during the day when the plants are actively growing. The surface waters where light is plentiful may even become supersaturated with oxygen, which diffuses out into the air. At night, when there is no oxygen production but lots of respiration, the "lost" oxygen made during the day when the plants were growing is no longer available, and oxygen levels may become very low if respiration demands exceed the rate at which oxygen can diffuse back into the water from the air. Even more problematic is the fact that the macroalgae and phytoplankton do not stay in the surface water where they grow. They sink into the deeper water as they die, or are eaten by grazing animals and excreted as fecal pellets. In stratified systems, this rain of organic matter stimulates respiration in the isolated bottom water and sediments, which depletes bottom water oxygen levels.

While it appears that the number of coastal areas experiencing hypoxia and anoxia is increasing, especially in Europe and North America, and that the aerial and temporal extent and intensity of hypoxia is increasing (Diaz 2001; Selman 2007), it must be remembered that oxygen concentrations vary a great deal in many coastal systems from day to day and, in fact, from hour to hour with light and tides. They also vary strongly in many areas with depth and with the history of wind and tidal mixing. It is also true that as the research and management communities became more aware of the nutrient-eutrophication-hypoxia/anoxia linkage, they focused more efforts on measuring dissolved oxygen. And advances in instrumentation have made it increasingly practical to deploy oxygen meters for continuous recording of dissolved oxygen over long periods of time. For hypoxia, as for many other things, the more you look, the more you find. On the other hand, it is also easy to miss hypoxic conditions—bottom waters that have experienced low oxygen for days may recover within minutes or hours with a strong wind. Hypoxia is a dark shadow that is difficult to scale and track precisely. But surveys of scientific opinion in the U.S. and Europe clearly show widespread concern about eutrophication and hypoxia (Bricker et al. 2007; Langmead and McQuatters-Gollop 2007; Selman 2007), and there is no reason to doubt that warming waters that are receiving ever more N and P are likely to be experiencing increasing hypoxia and anoxia. As Valiela (2006) put it: "It seems safe to conclude that most coastal waters are exposed to some degree of eutrophication, and that in most of these cases conditions are worsening."

1.3. WHY NITROGEN IS DIFFICULT TO CONTROL

1.3.1. Sources are irreplaceable, complex, and widespread

Anthropogenic N enters the coastal marine environment because of two essential human activities—the combustion of organic matter to release energy (including biomass, coal, oil, and natural gas) and the production and consumption of food (Galloway et al. 2002). In the case of coal combustion (and to a lesser extent crude oil combustion), some fossil N is released from the fuel itself, and some is "fixed" or made available to most plants by the oxidation of N in the atmosphere at high temperatures. Biomass burning releases N contained in the organic matter and fixes N from the atmosphere. The combustion of natural gas only fixes N from the atmosphere. Since N accounts for almost 80% of the atmosphere, the potential supply of N from this source is inexhaustible (e.g., Galloway et al. 2002). Because the release and production

Photo 1.4: A portion of the shoreline of Chesapeake Bay, the largest estuary in the United States. The inputs of nitrogen to a system like this come from many different sources and are difficult to control.

of reactive N is an inadvertent consequence of fuel combustion, N pollution and the problem of increasing atmospheric CO_2 are linked, though the choice of fuel and improving technology can change the link in important ways (Galloway and Cowling 2002). Because the oxidized atmospheric N appears as nitric acid in rain, N pollution and lake and forest acidification are also linked. Because fuel combustion puts reactive or biologically available N into the atmosphere, that N can easily travel great distances before it is deposited on land and water. This means that N can be deposited on coastal watersheds and coastal marine waters from sources far from the coast and outside of the watershed draining to a bay or estuary. The area from which various materials may be put into the atmosphere and reach a given estuary is called the airshed of that estuary. Because different materials behave differently in the atmosphere, the boundaries of the airshed vary for different pollutants. As an example, N modeling studies suggest that the airshed of Chesapeake Bay is 6.5 times larger than the watershed of the bay, which is itself 17 times bigger than the bay (Chesapeake Bay Program undated) (figure 1.1).

Combustion sources of reactive N are both fixed (e.g., electric power generation plants, industries) and mobile (e.g., road and air transport). The importance of various sources varies around the world. For example, road transport accounted for about 28% of N oxide emissions in Asia in 1990 but for 45% of emissions in Europe in 1998 (Bradley and Jones 2002). Electric power generation contributes a larger share of N oxide emissions in coal burning Asia ($\sim$ 31%) than it does in Europe and North America, which rely more on oil, natural gas, and nuclear energy for electric power generation (Bradley and Jones 2002).

Not surprisingly, the global distribution of the deposition of reactive N from the atmosphere corresponds closely to the global distribution of fossil fuel combustion (and human population density) (e.g., Galloway and Cowling

Figure 1.1: Airshed and watershed of Chesapeake Bay. The area of the airshed is over six times as great as the area of the Chesapeake Bay watershed.

Source: http://www.epa.gov/AMD/images/chesbay.oxN.gif.

2002). It is more difficult to assess the amount of N arriving from atmospheric deposition that actually enters a particular coastal water body. Some is deposited directly on the water surface, and the relative importance of this input compared to inputs from the watershed or catchment tends to vary directly with the size of the water body (e.g., Paerl 1995). However, some fraction of the N that is transported through the atmosphere and deposited on the larger watershed will also ultimately reach downstream coastal waters. This may be more important than the direct deposition and is much more difficult to quantify. It is usually estimated using indirect modeling techniques or, more rarely, measurements of stable N isotopes in rivers (e.g., Howarth 1998; Mayer et al. 2002; Boyer et al. 2002).

Food production makes the N in the atmosphere available to the biosphere in two ways: from the industrial production of inorganic N fertilizers in the Haber-Bosh process; and from the cultivation of specialized N-fixing crops such as soybeans and pulses (Smil 2002). The combined production of reactive N in agriculture is over five times greater than that associated with fuel combustion (about 100 Tg N y^{-1} in Haber-Bosch, over 30 Tg y^{-1} in biological fixation, and about 25 Tg y^{-1} from combustion; Galloway et al. 2002). The most recent assessment of the global N budget suggests that total anthropogenic sources of N may now be about 1.7 times the estimated background sources, due to lightning and natural terrestrial and marine N fixation. This represents a very large perturbation of one of the biosphere's most important biogeochemical cycles.

As with fuel combustion, the production of synthetic fertilizer increased rapidly with economic expansion following the Second World War (Smil 2002) as part of what has been called "The Great Acceleration" (Steffen, Crutzen, and McNeill 2007). The absolute importance of synthetic N fertilizer to the current human population has been emphasized by Smil (2001) after extensive analysis:

– We can thus conclude that the Haber-Bosch synthesis now provides the very means of survival for about 40% of humanity; …

Our ever-increasing use of synthetic fertilizers has been driven by two important factors: increasing human population and a growing world economy (Steffen, Crutzen, and McNeill 2007). While the role of the first is obvious, the second may be less appreciated. There is a correlation between wealth among countries and their use of synthetic fertilizer (e.g., Nixon 1995). Much of this correlation may be due to another correlation, that between income and per capita protein consumption (Nixon 1995). The latter is important because it is the consumption of protein that provides N in the diet—N that is (except in growing children) ultimately excreted into the environment. Still more important, however, is the link between income and the type of protein consumed: vegetable protein or meat protein. While there are important cultural factors that influence the consumption of meat and the forms of meat consumed, the general pattern is that meat consumption increases markedly with growing wealth. This is shown very dramatically by an analysis of changing per capita gross domestic product and per capita consumption of meat, milk, eggs, and rice in thirteen Asian countries (Shindo, Okamoto, and Kawashima 2006). While the first three rose strongly with income, rice consumption showed little change or declined sharply as in South Korea and Malaysia. Even in a rich country like the United States, meat consumption has been rising steadily (Howarth et al. 2002).

The great range in per capita meat consumption and in the type of meat consumed is clearly evident in even a summary comparison of recent data for various countries (table 1.1). The U.S. mean of 126 kg per person per year is equivalent to 345 g per person per day. Since fresh meat of various types is about 20% protein (e.g., Held 2007), this converts to almost 70 g protein per person per day compared to recommended total (including plant protein) dietary intakes of 50 g per day for women over age 25 and 63 g per day for

Photo 1.5: Concentrated animal feeding operation. Modern beef production causes the direct and indirect addition of large amounts of nitrogen to the landscape.

Table 1.1: Annual meat consumption in various countries. Units are kg per person in 1999

Country	Total	Beef	Pork
United States	126	45	32
Denmark	114	21	74
Spain	104	16	64
France	89	27	38
Portugal	74	15	31
United Kingdom	73	20	25
Mexico	53	21	10
China	45	4	31
Ukraine	32	13	14
Egypt	16	8	–
India	2	1.5	–

Source: U.S. Census 2000. Per capita consumption of meat and poultry, by country statistics.
Available at: http://www.allcountries.org/uscensus/1370_per_capita_consumption_of_meat_abd_html.

men over age 25 (National Academy of Sciences 1989). Of course, the population is not all over 25 years old, so the over consumption of protein is even greater than it appears. We are able to make a more detailed comparison of required vs. observed protein consumption for the city of Providence, Rhode Island (United States), where we have obtained extensive analyses of the N content of raw sewage entering the largest sewage treatment plant serving the city. These analyses suggest that the 100,000 plus population being served by the plant is consuming an average of just over 100 g of protein per person per day. This compares to an age (weight)- and gender-adjusted average recommended daily intake for the population of 50 g protein per person per day (Nixon et al. 2008). In other words, protein consumption in the city is roughly twice that needed for adequate nutrition, and twice as much N is being released in sewage as is required for the nutritional needs of the population. So high is the consumption of meat protein in the U.S. that a reduction of 40% would still leave the population with a per capita meat consumption equal to that of Great Britain; not a country known for vegetarianism!

The consumption of meat protein is of particular concern in terms of N pollution, not just because of the N excreted by meat-eating people. The production of meat is very inefficient in terms of N. In the United States, protein conversion efficiencies for edible portions of beef, pork, and chicken average about 5%, 10%, and 20%, respectively (Smil 2001). In other words, it requires 100 kg of N in corn (maize) to produce 5 kg of edible N in beef when averaged across the herd. The remaining 95 kg of N ultimately enters the landscape as metabolic waste from the cows or carcasses. In the last twenty years, the amount of grain being fed to animals has increased by 200-250 million tons (*The Economist* 2007). Moreover, the production of corn and other grains is not completely efficient in terms of N. Even in very efficient corn production in the U.S., recent N efficiency has been about 75%, meaning that about one quarter of the N applied as fertilizer does not enter the meat production food chain (Fixen and West 2002).

If this report had been written just a few years ago, our discussion of food production and coastal N pollution and eutrophication would have ended with the preceding paragraph. Today, however, we cannot leave this topic without noting the increasing link between what has been considered food production and fuel combustion.

This link arises because of the growing use of biomass (primarily sugar cane and corn or maize) to produce ethanol for use as an independent fuel or as a gasoline supplement in transportation. While this has been going on for over 25 years, the production of ethanol has increased dramatically in the last five years, especially in the United States (figure 1.2). Four countries, the U.S., Brazil, China, and India, now account for over 80% of global ethanol production (Murray 2005). While the combustion of ethanol in automobile engines oxidizes N from the atmosphere and makes it biologically available (as does the burning of gasoline), a major concern for marine ecologists is that both

Figure 1.2: Ethanol production throughout the world over the last twenty-five years

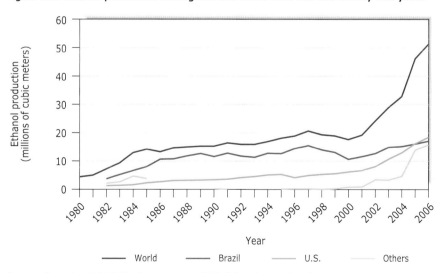

Source: Data for 1980-2004 from Murray (2005) for the Earth Policy Institute; data for 2005-06 from Renewable Fuels Association.

sugar cane (the major crop used in Brazil and other tropical countries) and maize (used in the U.S.) are crops that require large quantities of N fertilizer. Application of N in sugar cane production is commonly between 100 and 400 kg ha^{-1} y^{-1} (UN Food and Agricultural Organization online data, http://www.fao.org/docrep/007) and the average N application for U.S. corn is about 150 kg ha^{-1} y^{-1} (Fixen and West 2002). The rapid expansion of maize agriculture in the U.S. has come largely from the conversion of land formerly used for soybean and wheat production (*The Economist* 2007); crops requiring much less N fertilizer. Because soybeans grow in association with N-fixing bacteria, they may need relatively little or no synthetic N fertilizer (e.g., Staton and Warncke 2007), and N applications on wheat commonly range from about 50 to 75 kg ha^{-1} y^{-1} (Blumenthal and Sander 2002). It is worth asking how such land use change will impact the long-term plan to reduce nutrient loads to the Gulf of Mexico, and thus reduce the extent and severity of hypoxia in the northern Gulf (e.g., Rabalais et al. 2007; Justic et al. 2007).

The melding of the food and fuel economies is having dramatic impacts on the global price of food and on the ability of the U.S. to supply food to other countries. As noted in a recent essay, "The End of Cheap Food" (*The Economist* 2007): "The 30 m tonnes of extra maize going into ethanol this year amounts to half the fall in the world's overall grain stocks … : *fill up an SUV's fuel tank with ethanol and you have used enough maize to feed a person for a year.*"(emphasis added). While others have emphasized the questionable net energy yield of ethanol from maize, the impact of expanding sugar cane production on tropical forests, and the risks to global food security (e.g., Murray 2005), we believe that the rise of biomass-based ethanol production also poses risks for coastal marine ecosystems, especially the nutrient-sensitive tropical ones that lie downstream from sugar cane and other rapidly growing tropical plants.

1.3.2. Nitrogen moves in many forms and many ways

Throughout this report we have been referring to nitrogen as N, its symbol in the periodic table of elements. But N exists in many forms, and this chemical diversity complicates the measurement and management of the element as it moves from sources on land or in the atmosphere to the coast. The vast amount of N in the atmosphere exists as relatively inert N$_2$ gas that is only available to certain microbes with the special ability to "fix" or convert it into forms that are useable by other forms of life. Some of these N-fixing microbes live in close association with terrestrial plants, such as soybeans and alder trees, and can provide N for their needs. Some live in marine systems like coral reefs, salt marshes, and seagrass meadows or in surface waters of systems such as the Baltic Sea, and can add reactive N directly to the marine environment. Trace amounts of N also exist as N_2O, or nitrous oxide, a powerful greenhouse gas.

Reactive nitrogen produced by fuel combustion exists as various oxides of N or as ammonia and is in the form of gases, aerosols, and very fine particulates. There is also a significant amount of dissolved organic N in atmospheric deposition whose source(s) and fate is not well known. The transport and deposition of the different forms varies with temperature, the nature of the surface, and several other factors.

The production of synthetic fertilizer begins with the conversion of atmospheric N_2 into ammonium, but this can be converted into nitrate or urea and applied to fields in various ways. The amount of N that is lost from farm fields varies with the form of N applied, the method of application, the time of application, the type of crop being fertilized, and a number of other factors. Some of the N may be denitrified by special bacteria and returned to the atmosphere as N_2 gas. If animal manure is recycled as a source of organic N, much of that N may be lost to the atmosphere as ammonia gas that can be transported various distances before being redeposited, perhaps in coastal watersheds or directly in coastal waters. While some ammonium is absorbed in soils, some is oxidized to nitrite and nitrate, which can move easily through the soil in groundwater. Soil microbes also release dissolved organic N, a complex mix of poorly defined compounds from vegetation that may be easily taken up by other microbes or, in the case of some compounds, be very resistant to further biological activity. Much of the dissolved organic N also moves with groundwater and surface water to reach the coast, where its fate and impact are poorly known.

Nitrogen in the protein consumed by humans and other animals can reach the coastal marine environment by a variety of pathways. The N in animal waste can be deposited directly into streams, can be washed off impervious surfaces in concentrated animal feeding operations by wash water and storm water runoff, can be volatilized into the atmosphere, or enter groundwater. The N in human waste deposited in septic systems generally enters the groundwater, unless systems are specially designed for its removal. Similarly, the N in human waste that is collected by sewer systems can be transported even more efficiently into surface waters from sewage collection and, in some cases, treatment facilities. Because of its many sources and pathways, and because the airshed and watershed of most estuaries are much bigger than the estuary, N fertilization per area of estuaries is remarkably high: higher than the direct N fertilization of many major crops (table 1.2). Fortunately, advanced waste water treatment can be used to remove large amounts of the N in sewage, especially during warmer weather, though not without significant costs. Removing N from so-called "non-point sources" like agricultural runoff is much more challenging. In spite of all these complexities, an overall picture of the N links between airsheds, watersheds, and coastal ecosystems has emerged during the last decade or so. Surprisingly strong linear correlations have been found between the total input of anthropogenic N to watersheds (expressed per unit area) and the annual export of total N and dissolved inorganic N from the watershed (e.g. Peierls et al. 1991; Howarth 1998; Boyer et al. 2002). While the slope of the relationship appears to vary with temperature, such that warmer areas export a smaller fraction of the input (Schaefer and Alber 2007), the striking feature of the relationships is that relatively little of the N input leaves the watershed (Van Breemen 2002). Export in the northeastern U.S. averages about 25% of N input, against less than 10% in the southeastern U.S. (Schaefer and Alber 2007). The generality of these findings, particularly with respect to tropical watersheds with their strong wet-dry seasons, still needs to be determined, but they contain some good and some bad news for those concerned with coastal marine eutrophication. The good news is that watersheds with widely varying land use attenuate large amounts of N by sequestration and denitrification, and that warmer watersheds may be stronger sinks for N than we previously thought. The latter may be particularly important given the projected trends in tropical coastal areas discussed below. The bad news is that as more anthropogenic N enters a watershed, more N will reach the coast. It is also disquieting that such a large amount of N is retained and/or removed by processes that could be impacted by changing climate, potentially releasing previously stored N.

Table 1.2: N fertilization of agricultural crops and estuaries

Crops [1]	N, kg ha^{-1} y^{-1}	Estuaries [2]	N, kg ha^{-1} y^{-1}
Pineapple	500-650	Randers Fjord	2315
Bananas	300-600	Scheldt	1875
Rice	200-400	Lagoon of Venice	335
Potato	140-240	Narragansett Bay	275
Sugar cane	100-400	Chesapeake Bay	130
Corn (maize)	100-200	Baltic Sea	30
Spinach	60-100		

[1] *Source*: UN Food and Agricultural Organization, Department of Natural Resources Management and Environment: http://www.fao.org/documents and U.S. Department of Agriculture: http://www.ers.usda.gov/Data/FertilizerUse/.
[2] *Source*: Nixon and Pilson (1983).

1.4. SOME CONCERNS FOR THE FUTURE

A detailed effort has recently been made to compare historical, current, and future (2050) global and regional N budgets (Galloway et al. 2002). The result suggests a future with much more reactive N moving through the biosphere, perhaps 70% more than under recent conditions. The model used in this study suggests a more modest increase of about 30% in the reactive N reaching the coast in rivers, though the authors caution that the model assumed that current rates of N attenuation in watersheds remain unchanged. They point out that this assumption may fail, as wetlands (important sites of N removal in watersheds) are increasingly filled, and as N deposition from the atmosphere increases markedly with increasing fossil fuel combustion. Atmospheric deposition may become an increasingly important pathway by which N reaches coastal ecosystems, unless the investment is made in improved technology to uncouple N emissions from combustion.

Future N pollution and coastal marine eutrophication will vary greatly in different parts of the world, with the greatest increases in Asia. As in the past, N pollution will follow economic expansion and population growth. As pointed out by Crutzen (2002), almost all the symptoms of "The Great Acceleration" have so far been caused by just 25% of the world population. As hundreds of millions of people in the developing world rapidly strive to attain Western standards of living, there will almost certainly be many surprises that even our most sophisticated models cannot foresee. For example, recent projections of N fertilizer use in the U.S. showed that diet choices could have a very significant impact (Howarth et al. 2002), but this exercise took place just before the food-for-fuel folly hit American agriculture. And at this writing there is no evidence of Americans reducing their consumption of meat, despite major education efforts by health agencies and the insurance industry to reduce the consumption of animal fat, and the growing awareness that we confront a national epidemic of obesity. One can only assume that the developing nations will continue to consume increasing amounts of meat (figure 1.3). Demand for livestock products has been growing three times faster in developing countries than in the industrialized world (Holmes 2001).

The developing world will also be the place where human population growth is greatest, and the most rapid growth will be in urban areas, most of which are on or near the coast (Laurence 2007). Urban growth is particularly important because it will require public health infrastructure in the form of water supply and sewage collection/disposal (Nixon 1995). Bush toilets and trenches may suffice in the country, but not in cities. As in Europe and North America in the late 1800s, this will bring increasing amounts of N and P to the coast (Nixon et al. 2008).

Figure 1.3: Per capita meat consumption. Consumption figures over the last forty years and projected into the future for developing, industrialized, and transition countries.

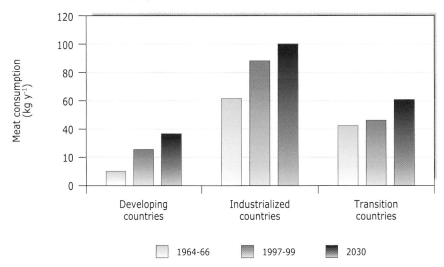

Source: WHO 2002. ftp://ftp.fao.org/docrep/fao/005/ac911e/ac911e00.pdf.

Most of the developing world lies in the tropics or subtropics, and it is the coastal marine ecosystems of these regions that will be most severely impacted by nutrient pollution in the coming decades. Many will be enriched by fertilizer runoff and livestock waste, some will be downstream of spreading aquaculture enterprises (also sources of N and P from fish or shrimp food and waste), almost all will be enriched by atmospheric N deposition from rapidly growing automobile fleets and increasing electric power generation, and some will receive increasing amounts of N and P from human sewage. Some tropical systems, especially coral reefs and seagrass meadows, may also be endangered by intensive development for coastal tourism. Globally, tourism accounts for approximately 35% of the world's exports of services and more than 70% in least developed countries (World Tourism Organization 2007). International tourism has also been part of "The Great Acceleration", increasing from fewer than 25 million travelers in 1950 to over 800 million in 2005 (figure 1.4). The most rapid increase has been in Asia and the Pacific at about 13% per year (World Tourism Organization 2007). Of course, not all tourism impacts the coastal environment, but the popularity of tropical beaches and coral reefs has certainly been growing. According to a recent assessment, 40% of the world's reefs are at risk from overexploitation, 30% are at risk from development, 20% suffer from inland pollution and erosion, and 10% are exposed to marine pollution (Bryant et al. 1998). Remarkably, just six coun-

Figure 1.4: International tourist arrivals between 1950 and 2005

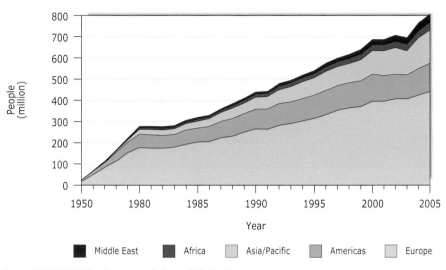

Source: WTO 2007. http://unwto.org/facts/eng/historical.htm.

tries contain over half the world's reefs: Australia, Indonesia, Philippines, Papua New Guinea, Fiji, and the Maldives. Reefs in Southeast Asia are the most threatened, with over 80% of them at risk, mainly from coastal development and overfishing (Bryant et al. 1998). Regions with high population density often have the most reef area (figure 1.5). Not surprisingly, there is a

Figure 1.5: Reef area by region and coastal population density

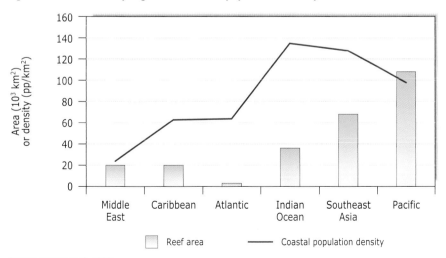

Source: Bryant et al. 1998.

Photo 1.6: Residential tourism development in a wetland area. Tropical coastal ecosystems will almost certainly experience increases in nutrient enrichment from growing tourism development, expanding agriculture, and rising coastal urban populations.

strong correlation between coastal population density and area of highly threatened reef (figure 1.6). While resort developers have probably learned the hard way not to let sewage contaminate the surrounding waters with pathogens, the threats posed by nutrient pollution have largely gone unnoticed (e.g., Goreau 2003). On the positive side, well-designed biological N removal in packaged sewage treatment plants constructed in association with resort development may be particularly effective at warm tropical temperatures.

In parts of Europe, North America, and other wealthy areas, the future of N pollution may be quite different, at least in urban estuaries where human sewage is the primary source of N. The rising awareness of problems associated with nutrient pollution during recent decades has led to increasing investment in advanced waste water treatment with N removal. Improved secondary treatment and removal of P from detergents has also led to declines in P loading (e.g., Nixon et al. 2008). Even in some areas with intensive agriculture, aggressive efforts to improve fertilizer efficiency and manure management have led to reduced nutrient pollution from these sources. For example, in Denmark: "Since 1991 land-based inputs of nitrogen and phosphorus to estu-

Figure 1.6: Reef area considered to be gravely threatened as a function of coastal population density

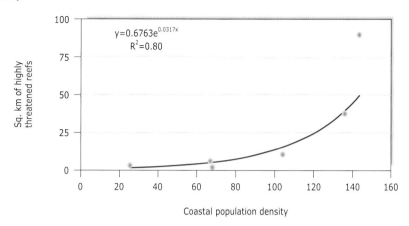

Source: Bryant et al. 1998.

aries and coastal areas have been reduced by 35% and 60% respectively. The reduction in nitrogen (21%) is mainly caused by reduced losses from agricultural soils, while the reduction in phosphorus is due to extension of sewage treatment."(Ærtebjerg, Andersen, and Hansen 2003, p. 107). These reductions in loading led (after a lag) to "significant decreases in nutrient concentrations on a large regional scale ...", including the open waters of the Kattegat, the Sound, and the Belt Sea, as well as estuaries (Carstensen et al. 2006, p. 398). Primary production in these same areas increased from the 1950s through the 1980s, then declined modestly coincident with declining nutrient loads through the 1990s (Rydberg, Ærtebjerg, and Edler 2006). Unfortunately, in the late 1990s changes were made in the methods used to measure primary production, making it hard to know if apparent increases after 1998 are real (Rydberg, Ærtebjerg, and Edler 2006). Conley et al. (2007) carried out a detailed statistical analysis of bottom water oxygen concentrations in Danish estuaries and open waters, to see if hypoxia was declining with decreasing nutrient loading and productivity. The result is instructive. While declining N loading appeared to be correlated with increasing oxygen concentrations in bottom waters during summer (as expected), declining wind speed and increasing water temperature combined to produce net declines in bottom water oxygen, and no improvement was realized. Although it follows that conditions would have been worse in the absence of the nutrient reduction, it is disappointing not to have found a more positive response to the management effort.

If eutrophication is an increase in the supply of organic matter to an ecosystem, a decline in the supply of organic matter is called "oligotrophication" (Nixon, in press). This phenomenon has received increasing attention in lakes, where nutrient pollution and eutrophication attracted management interest at least a decade earlier than in coastal marine ecosystems (e.g., Nay 1996; Anderson, Jeppesen, and Soendergaard 2005). Oligotrophication has received almost no attention in marine ecology, but this will surely change as management actions take effect. In some cases, the results of oligotrophication may be disappointing, as with hypoxia in the Baltic Sea or the Seto Inland Sea off Japan, where fish landings appear to have declined with nutrient reductions (Yamamoto 2003). In other cases, it may prove difficult to document cause and effect relationships. A case in point is the Dutch Wadden Sea, where extensive monitoring over many decades has shown a complex and somewhat confusing response to reduced nutrient loading (Philippart et al. 2007). While phytoplankton biomass and the productivity of both phytoplankton and phytobenthos increased markedly with increasing nutrient enrichment during the 1970s and early 1980s, declines in phytoplankton production were more modest following nutrient reduction, and total biomass remained relatively constant. However, the contribution of diatoms to biomass declined markedly with nutrient reduction. The complex interplay of "bottom-up" (nutrient enrichment) and "top-down" (grazing) processes made it difficult to correlate ecosystem changes, especially of upper trophic levels, with nutrient reduction. After assessing benthic animals and marine birds, Philippart et al. (2007) concluded:

> In contrast to the sequential increase in biomass of phytoplankton and macrozoobenthos during nutrient enrichment … subsequent nutrient reduction affected the biomass of these communities to a much lesser extent. The weak coupling between nutrient levels and biomass during the reduction phase might be a result of a delayed response … and concurrent changes in species composition … which can dampen the numerical and biomass responses at higher trophic levels.

It is a characteristic of complex systems that their history is an important influence on their future behavior, and we should not expect the path of oligotrophication to trace in reverse the exact steps of eutrophication. A further complication to predicting the response of coastal marine ecosystems to nutrient reduction and/or oligotrophication is that many other factors influencing the behavior of the ecosystem will almost certainly have been changing during the time of nutrient enrichment. Carlos Duarte and colleagues (2009) have assembled data on chlorophyll (as a measure of the biomass of phytoplankton) from a number of coastal systems that experienced nutrient enrichment followed by nutrient reduction. In no case did chlorophyll concentrations simply retreat with declining nutrient inputs along the same trajectory they followed while increasing during nutrient enrichment. They caution that, because of shifting baselines, managers (and scientists) who expect to restore coastal systems to a prior state simply by reducing nutrient inputs are trying to "Return to Neverland", home of the mythical Peter Pan and the Lost Boys. For these reasons, we must expect many surprises in the future from the temperate estuaries that have received so much of our attention (and our nutrients) in recent decades. And we cannot lose sight of the larger picture, that oligotrophication, like eutrophication, may be caused by factors other than changes in nutrient inputs. For example, two decades of oligotrophication in Narragansett Bay, Rhode Island (United States) appear to have been the result of increased temperature and clouds during a time of relatively stable nutrient inputs (Li and Smayda 1998; Fulweiler et al. 2007; Nixon et al. 2009; Fulweiler and Nixon, in press). And the supplies of nutrients themselves are influenced strongly by large-scale changes in climate and hydrography that may alter the carrying capacity of the environment; one of the most striking examples of which may be the decline of marine mammals and benthic animals with the climate-induced oligotrophication of the Bering Sea (Schell 2000; Grebmeier et al. 2006 respectively).

We close with a final observation that nutrient pollution lies at the intersection of two of the major themes of coastal ecology: the causes of productivity, and the impacts of pollution. It is not surprising that the topic embraces complications and conflicts. The eutrophication that nutrient pollution often causes is a fundamental change in the economy of the ecosystem, and it is not clear that the lessons we have learned from four decades of study in temperate coastal systems will hold as the very low nutrient waters of the tropics become enriched. For example, recent work off the Nile Delta has shown that anthropogenic nutrients may stimulate fisheries productivity (Oczkowski et al. 2009). Studying and managing nutrient pollution and eutrophication in tropical coastal environments is a major and immediate challenge for marine ecology. While it seems virtually certain that the world faces a future in which the cycles of N and P become increasingly perturbed, there are some reasons for optimism. The evidence from Europe, North America, and Japan is that as societies get richer, they invest more in pollution abatement. Hence, as the growing wealth of developing nations allows them to eat more meat and use more fertilizer, it may also allow them to invest more in the education and infrastructure that can mitigate nutrient and other forms of pollution. Moreover, because of the links between nutrient pollution and other environmental threats that we discussed earlier, many actions that may be taken to reduce carbon dioxide emissions and acid rain will also help to reduce N pollution. Actions taken to protect wetlands and riparian zones, due to their habitat values for wildlife, will also make watersheds hold or remove reactive N and P. To the extent that campaigns to improve human diet through education are successful, they will also reduce nutrient pollution. As the great limnologist G. E. Hutchinson (1969) pointed out, the term "eutrophic" was used in medicine to mean "well-nourished", long before it was taken up by ecologists. If the human population really becomes "eutrophic" by eating less meat and animal fat, it will go a long way to protecting the coastal marine environment from eutrophication.

ACKNOWLEDGEMENTS

The authors wish to thank Carlos Duarte and the BBVA Foundation for inviting them to contribute to this publication and for sponsoring S. Nixon's participation in the Colloquium which gave rise to it.

REFERENCES

ÆRTEBJERG, G., J. H. ANDERSEN, and O. HANSEN, eds. *Nutrients and Eutrophication in Danish Marine Waters. A Challenge for Science and Management.* National Environmental Research Institute, 2003. http://www.dmu.dk

ANDERSON, D. M., P. M. GLIBERT, and J. BURKHOLDER. "Harmful algal blooms and eutrophication." *Estuaries* 25 (2002): 704-726.

ANDERSON, N., E. JEPPESEN, and M. SOENDERGAARD. "Ecological effects of reduced nutrient loading (oligotrophication) on lakes: an introduction." *Freshwater Biology* 50 (2005): 1589-1593.

BINTZ, J. C., S. W. NIXON, B. A. BUCKLEY, and S. L. GRANGER. "Impacts of temperature and nutrients on coastal lagoon plant communities." *Estuaries* 26 (2003): 765-776.

BLUMENTHAL, J. M., and D. H. SANDER. *Fertilizing Winter Wheat I: Nitrogen, Potassium, and Micronutrients.* NebGuide G1460. University of Nebraska, Lincoln, 2002. http://www.ianrpubs.unl.edu/epublic/pages/publicationD.jsp?publicationid=424.

BOYER, E. W., C. L. GOODALE, N. A. JAWORSKI, and R. W. HOWARTH. "Anthropogenic nitrogen sources are relationships to riverine nitrogen export in the northeastern U.S.A." *Biogeochemistry* 57/58 (2002): 137-169.

BRADLEY, M. J., and B. M. JONES. "Reducing global NOx emissions: developing advanced energy and transportation technologies." *Ambio* 31 (2002): 141- 149.

BREITBURG, D. "Effects of hypoxia and the balance between hypoxia and enrichment on coastal fishes and fisheries." *Estuaries* 25 (2002): 767-781.

BRICKER, S., B. LONGSTAFF, W. DENNISON, A. JONES, K. BOICOURT, C. WICKS, and J. WOERNER. "Effects of Nutrient Enrichment in the Nation's Estuaries: A Decade of Change." *NOAA Coastal Ocean Program Decision Analysis Series No. 26.* National Centers for Coastal Ocean Science, Silver Spring, Maryland, 2007.

BRYANT, D., L. BURKE, J. MCMANUS, M. SPALDING, M. C. ABLAN, C. V. BARBER, C. CABOTE, et al. *Reefs at Risk: A Map-Based Indicator of Threats to the World's Coral Reefs.* World Resource Institute (WRI), International Center for Living Aquatic Resources Management (ICLARM), World Conservation Monitoring Centre (WCMC), and United Nations Environment Program (UNEP), 1998. http://pdf.wri.org/reefs.pdf.

CADDY, J. F. "Toward a comparative evaluation of human impacts on fishery ecosystems of enclosed and semi-enclosed seas." *Reviews in Fisheries Science* 1 (1993): 57-95.

CARACO, N. F., J. J. COLE, and D. L. STRAYER. "Top down control from the bottom: regulation of eutrophication in a large river by benthic grazing." *Limnology and Oceanography* 51 (2006): 664-670.

CARSTENSEN, J., D. CONLEY, J. ANDERSEN, and G. ÆRTEBJERG. "Coastal eutrophication and trend reversal: A Danish case study." *Limnology and Oceanography* 51 (2006): 398-408.

CHESAPEAKE BAY PROGRAM. "Modeling the Chesapeake Bay." Backgrounder, n.d. http://www.chesapeakebay.net.

CLOERN, J. E. "Our evolving conceptual model of the coastal eutrophication problem". *Marine Ecology Progress Series* 210 (2001): 223-253.

CONLEY, D., J. CARSTENSEN, G. ÆRTEBJERG, P. CHRISTENSEN, T. DALSGAARD, J. HANSEN, and A. JOSEFSON. "Long-term changes and impacts of hypoxia in Danish coastal waters." *Ecological Applications* 17 (2007): S165-S184.

CORREDOR, J. E., R. W. HOWARTH, R. R. TWILLEY, and J. M. MORELL. "Nitrogen Cycling and anthropogenic impact in the tropical interamerican seas." *Biogeochemistry* 46 (1999): 163-178.

CRONIN, L. E. "The role of man in estuarine processes". In G. H. Lauff, ed. *Estuaries.* American Association for the Advancement of Science Pub. No. 83, Washington, DC, 1967. 667-689.

CRUTZEN, P. J. "Geology of Mankind". *Nature* 415 (2002): 23.

DEEGAN, L. A. "Lessons learned: the effects of nutrient enrichment on the support of nekton by seagrass and salt marsh ecosystems." *Estuaries* 25 (2002): 727-742.

D'ELIA, C. F. "The cycling of essential elements in coral reefs." In L. Pomeroy and J. Alberts, eds. *Concepts of Ecosystem Ecology. Ecological Studies, 67.* New York: Springer Verlag, 1988.

DEJONG, F. *Marine Eutrophication in Perspective.* Heidelberg: Springer, 2006.

DIAZ, R. J. "Overview of hypoxia around the world." *Journal of Environmental Quality* 30 (2002): 275-281.

DUARTE, C. M. "Submerged aquatic vegetation in relation to different nutrient regimes." *Ophelia* 41 (1995): 87-112.

DUARTE, C. M., D. CONLEY, J. CARSTENSEN, and M. SÁNCHEZ-CAMACHO. "Return to Neverland: shifting baselines affect eutrophication restoration targets." *Estuaries and Coasts* 32 (2009): 29-36.

FIXEN, P. E., and F. B. WEST. "Nitrogen fertilizers: meeting contemporary challenges." *Ambio* 31 (2002): 169-176.

FULWEILER, R. W., S. W. NIXON, B. A. BUCKLEY, and S. L. GRANGER. "Reversal of the net dinitrogen gas flux in coastal marine sediments." *Nature* 448 (2007): 180-182.

FULWEILER, R. W., and S. W. NIXON. "Responses of benthic-pelagic coupling to climate change in a temperate estuary." *Hydrobiologia* (in press).

GALLOWAY, J., and E. COWLING, eds. *Optimizing Nitrogen Management in Food and Energy Productions, and Environmental Change. Ambio* 31(2), 2002.

—. "Reactive nitrogen and the world: 200 years of change." *Ambio* 31 (2002): 64-71.

GALLOWAY, J., E. COWLING, S. SEITZINGER, and R. SOCOLOW. "Reactive nitrogen: too much of a good thing?" *Ambio* 31 (2002): 60-63.

GOREAU, T. J. Case study on "Waste Nutrients: Impacts on Coastal Coral Reefs and Fisheries, and Abatement Via Land Recycling." UN Expert Meeting on Waste Management in Small Island Developing States, Havana, Cuba, 2003. http://www.globalcoral.org.

K. FREY, et al. "A major ecosystem shift in the northern Bering Sea." *Science* 311 (2006): 1461-1464.

HECK, K. L., and J. VALENTINE. "The primacy of top-down effects in shallow benthic ecosystems." *Estuaries and Coasts* 30 (2007): 371-381.

HELD, R. Untitled website, 2007. http://vis.berkeley.edu/courses/cs294-10-fa07/wiki/index.php/A2-RobinHeld.

HERMAN, P. M., J. J. MIDDLEBURG, J. VAN DE KOPPEL, and C. R. HEIP. "Ecology of estuarine macrobenthos." *Advances in Ecological Research* 29 (1999): 195-240.

HOLMES, K. "Carnivorous Cravings: Charting the World's Protein Shift." World Resources Institute – Earth Trends, 2001. http://earthtrends.wri.org/features/view_feature.php?theme=8&fid=24

HOWARTH, R. W. "An assessment of human influences on fluxes of nitrogen from the terrestrial landscape to estuaries and continental shelves of the North Atlantic Ocean." *Nutrient Cycling in Agroecosystems* 52 (1998): 213-223.

HOWARTH, R. W., and R. MARINO. "Nitrogen as the limiting nutrient for eutrophication in coastal marine ecosystems: evolving views over three decades." *Limnology and Oceanography* 51 (2006): 364-376.

HOWARTH, R. , D. ANDERSON, J. CLOERN, C. ELFRING, C. HOPKINSON, B. LAPOINTE, T. MALONE, et al. "Nutrient Pollution of Coastal Rivers, Bays, and Seas." *Issues in Ecology* 7 (2002). http://esa.sdsc.edu/

HOWARTH, R. W., E. W. BOYER, W. PABICH, and J. GALLOWAY. "Nitrogen use in the United States from 1961-2000 and potential future trends." *Ambio* 31 (2002): 88-96.

HUGHES, T., A. SZMANT, R. STENECK, R. CARPENTER, and S. MILLER. "Algal blooms on coral reefs: What are the causes?" *Limnology and Oceanography* 44 (1999): 1583-1586.

HUTCHINSON, G. E. "Eutrophication, past and present." In *Eutrophication: Causes, Consequences, Correctives*. National Academy of Sciences. Washington, DC: National Academies Press, 1969. 17-26.

INI (International Nitrogen Initiative). "The Issues of Nitrogen", 2007. www.initrogen.org

JOHNSTONE, J. *Conditions of Life in the Sea*, 1908. Reprint. New York: Arno Press, 1977.

JUSTIC, D., V. BIERMAN, D. SCAVIA, and R. HETLAND. "Forecasting Gulf's hypoxia: The next 50 years." *Estuaries and Coasts* 30 (2007): 791-801.

KENNISH, M. J., and A. R. TOWNSEND. "Nutrient enrichment and estuarine eutrophication." *Ecological Applications* 17 (2007).

KEMP, W. M., W. BOYNTON, J. ADOLF, D. BOESCH, W. BOICOURT, G. BRUSH, J. CORNWELL, et al. "Eutrophication of Chesapeake Bay: historical trends and ecological interactions." *Marine Ecology Progress Series* 303 (2005): 1-29.

LANGMEAD, O., and A. MCQUATTERS-GOLLOP, eds. *European Lifestyles and Marine Ecosystems – Exploring challenges for managing Europe's seas*, 2007. www.elme-eu.org

LAPOINT, B. E. "Nutrient thresholds for bottom-up control of macro algal blooms on coral reefs in Jamaica and southeast Florida." *Limnology and Oceanography* 42 (1997): 1119-1131.

LAPOINT, B. E. "Simultaneous top-down and bottom-up forces control macro algal blooms on coral reefs (Reply to the comment by Hughes et al.)." *Limnology and Oceanography* 44 (1999): 1586-1592.

LI, Y., and T. SMAYDA. "Temporal variability of chlorophyll in Narragansett Bay 1973-1990." *ICES Journal of Marine Science* 55 (1998): 661-667.

MAYER, B., E. W. BOYER, C. GOODALE, N. A. JAWORSKI, N. VAN BREEMEN, R. W. HOWARTH, S. SEITZINGER, et al. "Sources of nitrate in rivers draining sixteen watersheds in the northeastern U.S.: isotopic constraints." *Biogeochemistry* 57/58 (2002): 171-197.

MCINTYRE, A. D. "Effects of pollution on inshore benthos", In B. C. Coull, ed. *Ecology of Marine Benthos*. Colombia: University of South Carolina Press, 1977. 301-318.

MCQUATTERS-GOLLOP, A., D. E. RAITSOS, M. EDWARDS, Y. PRADHAN, L. MEE, S. LAVENDER, and M. ATTRILL. "A long-term chlorophyll dataset reveals regime shift in North Sea phytoplankton biomass unconnected to nutrient levels." *Limnology and Oceanography* 52 (2007): 635-648.

MELOSI, M. V. *The Sanitary City – Urban Infrastructure in America From Colonial Times to the Present*. Baltimore: The Johns Hopkins University Press, 2000.

MILLS, E. L. *Biological Oceanography: an Early History, 1870-1960*. Ithaca, NY: Cornell University Press, 1989.

MURRAY, D. "Ethanol's Potential: Looking Beyond Corn." Earth Policy Institute, Eco-Economy Updates, 2005. http://wwwearth-policy.org/Updates/2005/Update49.htm

NATIONAL ACADEMY OF SCIENCES. *Eutrophication: Causes, Consequences, Correctives*. Washington, DC: The National Academy Press, 1969.

NATIONAL RESEARCH COUNCIL. *Recommended Dietary Allowances*, 10th edition. Washington, DC: The National Academy Press, 1989.

NAY, J. J. "Oligotrophication and its discontents: effects of reduced nutrient loading on reservoir fisheries." *American Fisheries Society Symposium* 16 (1996): 285-295.

NIELSEN, O. I., M. S. KOCH, and C. J. MADDEN. "Inorganic phosphorus uptake in a carbonate-dominated seagrass ecosystem." *Estuaries and Coasts* 40 (2007): 827-839.

NIXON, S. W. "Coastal marine eutrophication: a definition, social causes, and future concerns." *Ophelia* 41 (1995): 199-219.

NIXON, S. W., and M. E. Q. PILSON. "Nitrogen in estuarine and coastal marine ecosystems." In E. Carpenter and D. Capone, eds. *Nitrogen in the Marine Environment*. New York: Academic Press, 1983. 565-648.

NIXON, S. W., C. A. OVAITT, J. FRITHSEN, and B. SULLIVAN. "Nutrients and the productivity of estuarine and coastal marine ecosystems." *Journal of the Limnological Society of Southern Africa* 12 (1986): 43-71.

NIXON, S. W., B. BUCKLEY, S. GRANGER, and J. BINTZ. "Responses of very shallow marine ecosystems to nutrient enrichment." *Human and Ecological Risk Assessment* 7 (2001): 1457-1481.

NIXON, S. W., and B. A. BUCKLEY. "'A strikingly rich zone' – nutrient enrichment and secondary production in coastal marine ecosystems." *Estuaries* 25 (2002): 782-796.

NIXON, S., B. BUCKLEY, S. GRANGER, L. HARRIS, A. OCZKOWSKI, R. FULWEILER, and L. COLE. "Nitrogen and phosphorus inputs to Narragansett Bay: past, present, and future." In A. Desbonnet and B. Costa-Pierce, eds. *Science for Ecosystem-based Management: Narragansett Bay in the 21st Century*. New York: Springer, 2008. 101-176.

NIXON, S. W., R. W. FULWEILER, B. A. BUCKLEY, S. L. GRANGER, B. L. NOWICKI, and K. M. HENRY. "The impact of changing climate on phenology, productivity, and benthic-pelagic coupling in Narragansett Bay." *Estuarine, Coastal and Shelf Science* (2009): doi:10.1016/j.ecss.2008.12.016.

NIXON, S. W. "Eutrophication and the macroscope." *Hydrobiologia* (in press).

OCZKOWSKI, A., and S. NIXON. "Increasing nutrient concentrations and the rise and fall of a coastal fishery; a review of data from the Nile Delta, Egypt." *Estuarine, Coastal, and Shelf Science* 77(3) (2008): 309-319.

OCZKOWSKI, A., S. NIXON, S. GRANGER, A.-F. EL-SAYED, and R. McKINNEY. "Anthropogenic enhancement of Egypt's Mediterranean fishery." *Proceedings of the National Academy of Sciences* 106 (2009): 1364-1367.

OLSEN, Y., S. AGUSTI, T. ANDERSEN, C. M. DUARTE, P. GASOL, I. GISMERVIK, A.-S. HEISKANEN, et al. "A comparative study of responses in planktonic food web structure and function in contrasting European coastal waters exposed to experimental nutrient addition." *Limnology and Oceanography* 51 (2006): 488-503.

PAERL, H. W. "Coastal eutrophication in relation to atmospheric nitrogen deposition: current perspectives." *Ophelia* 41 (1995): 237-260.

PEARSON, T. H., and R. ROSENBERG. "Macrobenthic succession in relation to organic enrichment and pollution of the marine environment." *Oceanography and Marine Biology Annual Review* 16 (1978): 229-311.

PEIERLS, B., N. CARACO, M. PACE, and J. COLE. "Human influence on river nitrogen." *Nature* 350 (1991): 386-387.

PHILIPPART, C., J. BEUKEMA, G. CADEE, R. DEKKER, P. GOEDHART, J. VAN IPEREN, M. LEOPOLD, and P. HERMAN. "Impacts of nutrient reduction on coastal communities." *Ecosystems* (2006): doi: 10.1007/s10021-006-9006-7.

PRITCHARD, D. W. "What is an estuary: a physical viewpoint." In G. H. Lauff, ed. *Estuaries*. Pub. No. 83, American Association for the Advancement of Science, Washington, DC, 1967. 3-5

RABALAIS, N. N., and R. E. TURNER. "Hypoxia in the northern Gulf of Mexico: description, causes and change." In N. N. Rabalais and R. E. Turner, eds. *Coastal Hypoxia: Consequences for Living Resources and Ecosystems*. Coastal and Estuarine Studies 58. Washington, DC: American Geophysical Union, 2001. 1-36.

RABALAIS, N. N. and S. W. NIXON, eds. "Nutrient Over-Enrichment in Coastal Waters: Global Patterns of Cause and Effect." *Estuaries* 25 (4B) (2002).

RABALAIS, N. N., R. E. TURNER, B. SEN GUPTA, D. BOESCH, P. CHAPMAN, and M. MUR-RELL. "Hypoxia in the northern Gulf of Mexico: Does the science support the plan to reduce, mitigate, and control hypoxia?" *Estuaries and Coasts* 30 (2007): 753-772.

RENEWABLE FUELS ASSOCIATION. Industry Statistics, 2007. http://www.ethanolrfa.org/industry/statistics/.

RICHARDSON, A. J., and D. S. SCHOEMAN. "Climate impact on plankton ecosystems in the Northeast Atlantic." *Science* 305 (2004): 1609-1612.

ROGERS, C. S., and J. MILLER. "Permanent 'phase shifts' or reversible declines in coral cover? Lack of recovery of two coral reefs in St. John, US Virgin Islands." *Marine Ecology Progress Series* 306 (2006): 103-114.

RYDBERG, L., G. ÆRTEBJERG, and L. EDLER. "Fifty years of primary production measurements in the Baltic entrance region, trends and variability in relation to land-based input of nutrients." *Journal of Sea Research* 56 (2006): 1-16.

RYTHER, J. H. "The ecology of phytoplankton blooms in Moriches Bay and Great South bay, Long Island, New York." *Biological Bulletin* 106 (1954): 198-209.

RYTHER, J. H. "Historical perspective of phytoplankton blooms on Long Island and the green tides of the 1950s". In E. Cosper, V. Bricelj, and E. Carpenter, eds. *Novel Phytoplankton Blooms*. New York: Springer Verlag, 1989. 375-382.

RYTHER, J. H., and W. M. DUNSTAN. "Nitrogen, phosphorus, and eutrophication in the coastal marine environment." *Science* 171 (1971): 1008-1012.

SCHAEFER, S. C., and M. ALBER. "Temperature controls a latitudinal gradient in the proportion of watershed nitrogen exported to coastal ecosystems." *Biogeochemistry* 85 (2007): 333-346.

SCHELL, D. M. "Declining carrying capacity in the Bering Sea: Isotopic evidence from whale baleen." *Limnology and Oceanography* 45 (2000): 459-462.

SCHINDLER, D. "Recent advances in the understanding and management of eutrophication." *Limnology and Oceanography* 51 (2006): 356-363.

SCOPE (Scientific Committee on Problems of the Environment, International Council of Scientific Unions). "Human Alteration of the Nitrogen Cycle – Threats, Benefits and Opportunities." UNESCO-SCOPE Policy Briefs, 2007. http://www.icsu-scope.org.

SELMAN, M. "Eutrophication: An Overview of Status, Trends, Policies, and Strategies." World Resources Institute, Washington, DC, 2007.

SHINDO, J., K. OKAMOTO, and H. KAWASHIMA. "Prediction of the environmental effects of excess nitrogen caused by increasing food demand with rapid economic growth in eastern Asian countries, 1961-2020." *Ecological Modelling* 193 (2006): 703-720.

STEFFEN, W., P. J. CRUTZEN, and J. R. MCNEILL. "The anthropocene: are humans now overwhelming the great forces of nature?" *Ambio* 36 (2007): 614-621.

SZMANT, A. M. "Nutrient enrichment on coral reefs: Is it a major cause of coral reef decline?" *Estuaries* 25 (2002): 743-766.

SMIL, V. *Enriching the Earth – Fritz Haber, Carl Bosch, and the Transformation of World Food Production.* Cambridge, MA: MIT Press, 2001.

SMIL, V. "Nitrogen and food production: proteins for human diets." *Ambio* 31 (2002):126-131.

SMITH, S. V., W. KIMMERER, E. LAWS, R. BROCK, and T. WALSH. "Kaneohe Bay sewage diversion experiment: perspectives on ecosystem responses to nutrient perturbation." *Pacific Science* 35 (1981): 279-402.

SMITH, V. H., S. B. JOY, and R. W. HOWARTH, eds. "Eutrophication of Freshwater and Marine Ecosystems." *Limnology and Oceanography* 51(1 part 2) (2006).

STATON, M., and D. WARNCKE. "Fertilizing Soybeans in Michigan." Soybean fact sheet, Michigan State University Extension, 2007. http://web1.msue.msu.edu/soybean2010/.

STIMSON, J., S. LARNED, and K. MCDERMID. "Seasonal growth of the coral reef macroalga *Dictyosphaeria cavernosa* (Forskål) Børgesen and the effects of nutrient availability, temperature and herbivory on growth rate." *Journal of Experimental Marine Biology and Ecology* 196 (1996): 53-77.

TARR, J. A. *The Search for the Ultimate Sink – Urban Pollution in Historical Perspective.* Akron OH: The University of Akron Press, 1996.

TARR, J. A. "Urban pollution – many long years ago." *American Heritage* 22 (1971): 65-69.

THE ECONOMIST. "The end of cheap food." *The Economist*, Dec. 8, 2007: 11-12.

TURNER, R. E. "Element ratios and aquatic food webs." *Estuaries* 25 (2002): 694-703.

TWILLEY, R. R., W. M. KEMP, K. STAVER, J. STEVENSON, and W. BOYNTON. "Nutrient enrichment of estuarine submerged vascular plant communities: I. Algal growth and effects on production of plants and associated communities." *Marine Ecology Progress Series* 23 (1985): 179-191.

UNEP and WHRC (United Nations Environmental Program and Woods Hole Research Center). *Reactive Nitrogen in the Environment: Too Much or Too Little of a Good Thing.* United Nations Environment Program, Paris, 2007. http://www.whrc.org.

VALIELA, I. *Global Coastal Change.* Oxford: Blackwell Publishing, 2006.

VAN BREEMEN, N., E. W. BOYER, C. L. GOODALE, N. A. JAWORSKI, K. PAUSTIAN, S. P. SEITZINGER, K. LAJTHA, et al. "Where did all the nitrogen go? Fate of nitrogen inputs to large watersheds in the northeastern U.S.A." *Biogeochemistry* 57-58 (2002): 267-293.

VITOUSEK, P. M., J. ABER, R. HOWARTH, G. LIKENS, P. MATSON, D. SCHINDLER, W. SCHLESINGER, and D. TILMAN. "Human Alterations of the Global Nitrogen Cycle: Causes and Consequences." *Issues in Ecology* 1, Washington, DC: Ecological Society of America, 1997. http://www.sdsc.edu/~ESA/.

WARWICK, R. M., and K. R. CLARKE. "Relearning the ABC: taxonomic changes and abundance/biomass relationships in disturbed benthic communities." *Marine Biology* 118 (1994): 739-744.

WHO (World Health Organization). "Diet, nutrition, and the prevention of chronic diseases." WHO Technical Report #916, 2002. ftp://ftp.fao.org/docrep/fao/005/ac911e/ac911e00.pdf.

WOLOWICZ, M., A. SOKOLOWSKI, A. BAWAZIR, and R. LASOTA. "Effect of eutrophication on the distribution and ecophysiology of the mussel *Mytilus trossulus* (Bilva) in southern Baltic Sea (the Gulf of Gdansk)." *Limnology and Oceanography* 51 (2006): 580-590.

WOOD, L. B. *The Restoration of the Tidal Thames.* Adam Hilger, Bristol, 1982.

WTO (World Tourism Organization), 2007. http://unwto.org/facts/eng/historical.htm.

WULFF, F. "Overall conclusions". In C. Lancelot, G. Billen, and H. Barth, eds. *Eutrophication and Algal Blooms in North Sea Coastal Zones, the Baltic, and Adjacent Areas: Prediction and Assessment of Preventive Actions.* Water Pollution Research Report No. 12, European Communities Environmental Program, Brussels, 1990. 267-271.

YAMAMOTO, T. "The Seto Inland Sea – eutrophic or oligotrophic?" *Marine Pollution Bulletin* 47 (2003): 37-42.

2. LOSS OF SEAGRASS MEADOWS FROM THE SPANISH COAST: RESULTS OF THE *PRADERAS* PROJECT

Núria Marbà
Mediterranean Institute for Advanced Studies (IMEDEA)
Spanish National Research Council (CSIC)-University of the Balearic Islands (UIB)
Esporles, Mallorca, Spain

2.1. INTRODUCTION

Seagrass meadows constitute the dominant ecosystem of shallow sandy seabeds in all seas, the polar zones excepted, where they fulfill important trophic and structural functions. Since the 1980s, the area of an increasing number of the planet's seagrass meadows has diminished partially or completely. Strong and intense meteorological perturbations, like hurricanes, and the spread of infections are responsible for some of this decline. However, the main cause of the loss of meadows on a global scale is attributed to perturbations of anthropogenic origin, such as coastal eutrophication, arising from the growth and development of the human population. Climate change, as reflected in the increased frequency and intensity of storms and the global warming the planet has experienced in recent decades, may contribute to accelerating seagrass meadow loss. At present, it is difficult to quantify the scale of this loss accurately because the global area occupied by seagrass meadows and the status of most of them are not known.

In 2006, the BBVA Foundation funded a three-year project as part of its Second Call for Research Proposals in Conservation Biology titled "Conservation of underwater meadows: the causes of their decreasing size and the effects on ecosystem functions", known as the *Praderas* (meadows) project for short. The ultimate aim of this project was to evaluate the conservation status of seagrass meadows, particularly those of the Spanish littoral zone, to identify the main threats to their conservation, evaluate the relationship between their conservation status and their roles in the ecosystem, and develop management guidelines for their conservation. This chapter presents the results obtained regarding the conservation status of *Posidonia oceanica* meadows, describes the principal factors that threaten them, and discusses the future of seagrasses in the light of the global change scenarios predicted for the 21st century.

◄ Photo 2.1: Spreading rhizomes of *Posidonia oceanica* colonized by epiphytic organisms

2.2. SEAGRASS MEADOWS: *POSIDONIA OCEANICA*

Seagrass meadows are made up of angiosperms, plants with flowers and fruits that can only complete their life cycles in the sea. Four species occur on the Spanish coast: *Posidonia oceanica*, *Cymodocea nodosa*, *Zostera marina*, and *Z. noltii*. While *C. nodosa*, *Z. marina*, and *Z. noltii* form meadows on the Mediterranean and Atlantic coasts, *P. oceanica* is endemic to the Mediterranean Sea. *P. oceanica* meadows occupy some 2,800 km² of the Spanish Mediterranean coast at depths between 0 and 45 m, and account for more than 90% of the total area of seagrass meadows along the Spanish coast.

Seagrass landscapes may be continuous or patchy but are usually extensive, composed of apparently identical shoots of a small number of genetically differentiated individuals, the clones or genets (photo 2.2). Marine angiosperms are clonal plants, whose stems, called rhizomes, spread and ramify across the sediment surface and keep neighboring shoots physiologically connected. Unlike non-clonal plants, in which new individuals arise exclusively by sexual reproduction through the germination of seeds, clonal plants produce most of their new individuals vegetatively by means of rhizomatous spread. This

Photo 2.2: Seagrass meadow of *P. oceanica,* Formentera, Balearic Islands. Declared a World Heritage Site by UNESCO.

form of growth allows marine angiosperms to occupy space with little investment in sexual reproduction. Although sexual reproduction does not contribute significantly to the increase or maintenance of shoot abundance in clonal plant populations, it is essential for initiating the formation of new clones and so is also necessary for the development and maintenance of seagrass beds.

The architectural pattern and growth forms of marine angiosperms are very similar. All species have shoots that are connected to a rhizome fragment from which roots are produced. The flowers or inflorescences sprout from the shoot (photo 2.3.A), and in most marine angiosperm species, including *P. oceanica*, they do it laterally, allowing the shoots to survive and grow after flowering. With the exception of one genus (*Halophila*), all marine angiosperm species have strap-like leaves, with basal meristems. Their great architectural uniformity contrasts with their wide range of sizes and growth rates, which are inversely scaled to species size (Duarte 1991) as a consequence of the greater cost (i.e., carbon and nutrient requirements) of producing bigger modules. *P. oceanica* is one of the planet's biggest marine angiosperms, with leaves measuring more than 1 m in length and woody rhizomes of 10 mm diameter (Duarte 1991). The

Photo 2.3.A: Inflorescence of *P. oceanica*

Photo 2.3.B: Fruits of *P. oceanica*, also known as sea olives.

horizontal rhizomes of *P. oceanica* grow between 1 and 6 cm annually and ramify once every 25 years on average (Marbà and Duarte 1998). The slow growth of *P. oceanica* rhizomes causes a slow radial expansion of its clones. *P. oceanica*, like the rest of its congeneric species growing on the southwest coast of Australia, flowers in the autumn. *P. oceanica* meadows exhibit scant flowering compared to other marine angiosperm species. Between 1957 and 2004, on average only 17% of *P. oceanica* meadows in the western Mediterranean flowered in any single year (Díaz-Almela, Marbá, and Duarte 2007a), and in the meadows that did flower an average of only 11% of shoots bore inflorescences. Due to this low flowering intensity and losses of 90% of fruit set (Díaz-Almela, pers. comm.), the rate of formation of new *P. oceanica* clones is very low, ranging from 0.004 to 0.02 m^{-2} year^{-1} in years of elevated reproduction (Díaz-Almela et al. 2008a). The low formation rate of *P. oceanica* clones is reflected in the genetic structure of seagrass meadows. The genetic study of *P. oceanica* meadows demonstrates that genetic diversity, calculated as the number of clones identified with respect to the number of shoots sampled, is fairly poor: in an area of 1,600 m^2 it may vary between 0.1 and 0.75 (Rozenfeld et al. 2007), depending on the meadow. Other genetic research on seagrass meadows shows that *P. oceanica* clones can reach a huge size, and it is not unusual to find genetically identical shoots at locations more than one kilometer apart (Díaz-Almela et al. 2007b). In the seagrass bed of the Es Freus–Ses Salines Marine Reserve (Ibiza–Formentera), a UNESCO World Heritage Site, identical genotypes have even been found in locations 15 km apart (Arnaud-Haond et al., in review).

P. oceanica optimizes its greater investment of resources (carbon and nutrients) by producing large modules with very long-lived shoots and clones. *P. oceanica* has the longest-living shoots of all marine angiosperms on the planet, reaching up to 60 years on average (Marbà et al. 2005). The detection, using molecular techniques, of *P. oceanica* clones spreading over dozens of meters and several kilometers of coastline, indicates that they may live for thousands of years. Based on the clonal growth rate of the species and its size, the large *P. oceanica* clone found in Formentera would be between 80,000 and 200,000 years old, making it the oldest organism on the planet (Arnaud-Haond et al., in review). Thousands-of-years-old *P. oceanica* meadows have also been identified by measuring the remains of rhizomes and roots in their deepest strata for the quantity of carbon-14 isotope remaining in the tissues (Mateo et al. 1997). Their long life allows the components of *P. oceanica* meadows to endure and spread over large areas, despite the species' low rates of clonal growth and new clone formation.

Photo 2.4: Painted comber (*Serranus scriba*) in a *P. oceanica* meadow

Due to the slow colonization and growth of *P. oceanica* clones, their meadows take centuries to form. Indeed *P. oceanica* colonization times can only be calculated using simulation models. From the rules governing the plant's clonal growth (rate of elongation of the horizontal rhizome, rate and angle of ramification, length of the section of rhizome connecting neighboring shoots), it is possible to simulate the spread of individual clones. This exercise reveals that a circular clone of *P. oceanica* would take 100 years to attain a diameter of 8 m (Sintes, Marbà, and Duarte 2006). Models simulating the development of a *P. oceanica* meadow composed of several clones growing in accordance with the species' growth rules indicate that *P. oceanica* would take 600 years to occupy 60% of the available space (Kendrick, Marbà, and Duarte 2005). The rate of seagrass meadow spread would vary throughout the colonization process. Its coverage would increase much more rapidly during the first 400 years of the meadow's life than in later years (Kendrick, Marbà, and Duarte 2005), when individuals would have to compete for space. The colonization time of *P. oceanica* is extremely long and thus its recolonization time in disturbed areas, to the extent that the loss of areas of *P. oceanica* is irrecoverable over a human timescale.

2.3. ECOLOGICAL FUNCTIONS OF *POSIDONIA OCEANICA* MEADOWS

P. oceanica meadows perform important ecological functions in the coastal area and on a global scale, over both short and long time periods. The roles of marine angiosperm meadows are described in detail in chapter 3 of this book (Dennison), and I will confine myself here to describing the long-term importance of *P. oceanica* beds, for the invaluable services they provide to the Mediterranean coastal area. *P. oceanica* meadows sustain a considerable biomass: on average, the leaf biomass of the meadow is 390 g dry weight m^{-2}, and the living biomass of rhizomes and roots is 1,700 g dry weight m^{-2} (Duarte and Chiscano 1999). The biomass of *P. oceanica* meadows per unit area is similar to that of coral reefs, which ranks them among the marine plant communities that sustain the greatest biomass by area on the planet (Duarte and Chiscano 1999). *P. oceanica* meadows have a three-dimensional structure, forming terraces, channels and barrier reefs that can reach a height of 3-4 m (photo 2.5). *P. oceanica* meadows accordingly modify the seabed topography. This three-dimensional structure arises from the growth of vertical rhizomes and from the fact that spread rates are similar in an upward and sideways direction (Kendrick, Marbà, and Duarte 2005) and that meadow rhizomes decompose only slowly.

Photo 2.5: Thousand-year-old *P. oceanica* reef, Formentera, Balearic Islands

P. oceanica meadows are highly productive systems, fixing 400 g C m^{-2} annually (Barrón et al. 2006). Although most (80%) of the fixed carbon is respired by the community itself, the net annual production of seagrass meadows is about 72 g C m^{-2}, representing a net carbon fixation 60 times that measured in coastal marine sediments devoid of vegetation (Barrón et al. 2006). The high productivity of seagrass meadows alters CO_2 and O_2 flow rates in the water column. For example, during daytime, the partial pressure of CO_2 at the sea–atmosphere interface of Palma Bay (Balearic Islands) is lower in areas with seabeds colonized by seagrass meadows than in areas with seabeds without vegetation (Gazeau et al. 2005).

A large part (42%-62%) of the net carbon fixed in *P. oceanica* meadows is retained and buried there (Larkum, Orth, and Duarte 2006; photo 2.5). Considering that they occupy an area of 50,000 km^2 in the Mediterranean Sea, these meadows bury some 2 Tg C year^{-1}. There are no estimates of the amount of carbon sequestered in other Mediterranean coastal and oceanic habitats, so it is hard to get an accurate handle on the importance of seagrass meadows as carbon sinks on a basin-wide scale. It must be substantial, however, considering that almost half the carbon sequestered globally in the oceans is buried in coastal plant habitats, and that seagrass species together account for 15% of

Photo 2.6: *P. oceanica* detritus accumulated on a beach

the total carbon buried in the ocean (Duarte, Middelburg, and Caraco 2005). Hence *P. oceanica* meadows absorb and bury a portion of atmospheric CO_2, helping with the regulation of the planet's climate.

P. oceanica meadows prevent coastal erosion. The relief and foliar canopy of the meadows reduce current velocity and, in shallow beds, help calm the swell (Larkum, Orth, and Duarte 2006). *P. oceanica* barrier reefs, located several meters from the shore, act as a break so the waves reaching the beach are of low intensity. The foliar canopy stimulates the deposition of particles suspended in the water through a number of mechanisms. The reduction of water current speed near the foliar canopy enables some suspended particles to be sedimented. Seagrass leaves are surfaces that interrupt the trajectories of suspended particles, which consequently end up deposited on top of the sediments (Hendriks et al. 2008). Part of the fauna associated with the meadow, particularly filtering organisms that live on the plant's leaves, actively trap suspended particles. Seagrass meadows retain the deposited particles and sediments that they colonize because the canopy prevents their resuspension, and because they are fixed by the network of rhizomes and roots that form the meadow's rhizosphere, to a depth of several meters. The effect of seagrass meadows on particle deposition and retention also increases the settling rate of larvae and propagules in this ecosystem. Seagrass meadows, as such, also help to increase marine biodiversity.

Part of a meadow's net annual production is exported to adjacent systems, among which are emerged beaches and dune systems. After heavy storms in the autumn, when *P. oceanica* renews its leaves, leaf litter and rhizome fragments pile up on the shore, forming what are known as "banquettes" (photo 2.6). On beaches adjacent to extensive seagrass meadows, these deposits can comprise up to 400 kg dry weight m^{-1} of coastline and amount to 50% of the material produced annually by the adjacent seagrass meadow (Larkum, Orth, and Duarte 2006). This biomass, produced in the meadow, supplies significant quantities of sediment and nutrients to the beach and associated dune system, particularly in regions where sediment production is of biogenic origin, as in the Balearic Islands. Considering that these islands have 100 km of beaches, seagrass meadows provide their sand dune systems with some 100,000 tonnes of biogenic material annually. Furthermore, 10% by weight of the biogenic material deposited on beaches is calcium carbonate originating from the structures of the epiphytic organisms that colonize the leaves and rhizomes of *P. oceanica*, plus the calcium carbonate precipitated on the leaves (Larkum, Orth, and Duarte 2006; photo 2.7). This suggests that *P. oceanica* meadows

Photo 2.7: *P. oceanica* **leaves colonized by epiphytic organisms with calcium carbonate structures**

may provide a substantial amount of the sand on the beaches. Moreover, this *P. oceanica* detritus covers the sand of the emerged beach, protecting it from erosion during heavy storms. Some of the *P. oceanica* detritus that accumulates on the shore stays in the water, increasing its viscosity and, thereby, reducing the intensity of the swell and also the risk of coastline erosion.

P. oceanica meadows are accordingly a key ecosystem for the functioning of and provision of services to the coastal zone and the Mediterranean basin. Prominent among these services are the burial of atmospheric CO_2 and maintenance of beaches, the latter being a vital element for the tourist industry. Conserving these functions and services depends on successfully conserving seagrass meadows.

2.4. THE STATE OF SPANISH COASTAL SEAGRASS MEADOWS: HOW BIG IS THE DECLINE?

Seagrass meadows are extremely vulnerable. Proof is that, since the 1980s, 102 of a total of 176 *P. oceanica* meadows reported in the Mediterranean basin have suffered a decline in the expanse and/or abundance of shoots. More than 50%

of the area of 17% of *P. oceanica* meadows has been lost over this period (Díaz-Almela, unpublished results).

The decline of *P. oceanica* meadows tends to be a gradual process. The cause of shrinkage is a progressive loss of shoots, so to prevent losses on a major scale, which are often irretrievable over human timescales, it is crucial to detect the problem at its initial stages. To achieve this means monitoring the state of seagrass meadows, using indicators that can quantify their current status and allow declines to be detected in time. The decline of long-lived seagrass meadows, like those of *P. oceanica*, can be detected early (on a yearly scale) by examining the demographic dynamics of their shoots in permanent plots (Short and Duarte 2001). An annual census of shoots in plots permanently installed in seagrass meadows (photo 2.8) allows to estimate the survival, birth, and death rates of a given population, and thereby its net growth rate, equivalent to the difference between birth and death rates. The net growth rate of the population indicates whether the meadow is declining (negative net growth), growing (positive net growth), or stable (net growth = 0).

Since the year 2000, the annual demographic balance has been quantified in 46 *P. oceanica* meadows growing at depths of between 5 and 25 m, 40 of them along the Spanish coast (figure 2.1). The density of their shoots at the beginning of the

Photo 2.8.A: Permanent plots established in a *P. oceanica* seagrass meadow to evaluate the demographic balance of shoots

Photo 2.8.B: Detail of tagged shoots in a *P. oceanica* test plot

Figure 2.1: Distribution of Mediterranean *P. oceanica* meadows whose demographic status has been evaluated over the past seven years

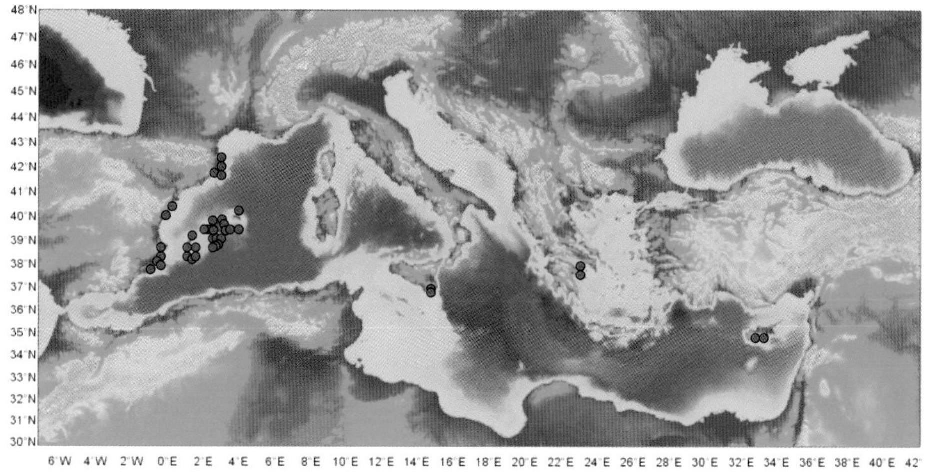

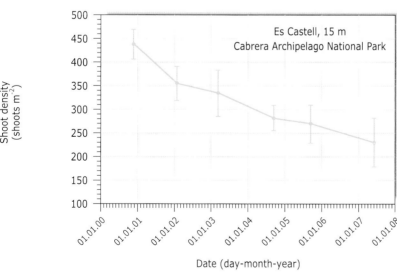

Source: http://www.chesapeakebay.net/info/wqcriteriapv/modeling.cfm.

study varied between 60 and 1,725 shoots m^{-2}. In the last seven years, 67% of the meadows studied have suffered net losses of shoot density, exceeding 20% in 47% of cases. These losses were observed in seagrass meadows situated not only in coastal areas experiencing strong anthropogenic pressure, but also in protected areas (figure 2.2) like the Cabrera Archipelago National Park (Balearic

Figure 2.2: Density of shoots in the seagrass meadow of Es Castell, at a depth of 15 m, Cabrera Archipelago National Park, since the year 2000

Photo 2.9: *P. oceanica* meadow growing on the coastal sea floor along the north coast of Ibiza, Balearic Islands

Islands), where measures to conserve the marine and terrestrial ecosystems have been in force since 1991. During this period, *P. oceanica* meadows experienced shoot mortality rates varying between less than 1% year^{-1} (e.g., Es Castell 20 m, Cabrera) and 84% year^{-1} (Pollença Bay, Mallorca), equivalent to absolute shoot mortality rates between 4 and 320 dead shoots m^{-2} year^{-1} (e.g., Es Castell 10 m, Cabrera and La Fossa, Alicante respectively). The mean annual mortality rate in seagrass meadows during the current decade stands at 11%, equivalent to 46 dead shoots m^{-2} year^{-1}. The observed mortality rates indicate that *P. oceanica* shoot half-life (i.e., the age to which 50% of a population's shoots survive) is greater than six years in most meadows, and may even reach 20 years in some sites like Formentera. On the other hand, the annual birth rate of shoots since 2000 has varied from less than 1% (e.g., Es Castell 20 m, Cabrera) to 48% (Pollença Bay, Mallorca), resulting in absolute birth rates of less than 2 new shoots m^{-2} year^{-1} (e.g., Es Castell 15 m, Cabrera) and 200 new shoots m^{-2} year^{-1} (Santa María Bay 7 m, Cabrera). In 50% of the seagrass meadows studied, the annual birth rate of shoots during the current decade has been lower than 6% or 25 new shoots m^{-2} year^{-1}. These low shoot birth rates indicate that most *P. oceanica* populations would take more than a decade to renew their shoots, and more than a century in the case of some off the island of Cabrera. Over the past ten years, shoot birth rates have lagged mortality rates in most seagrass meadows. Their annual net growth since 2000 has varied between -43% (Pollença Bay, Mallorca) and 46% (e.g., Es Castell 10 m, Cabrera), though most meadows have recorded under -5% annually, equivalent to a net loss of 12 shoots m^{-2} $year^{-1}$. Net loss rates also suggest that, if the current environmental conditions persist, seagrass meadows that are in decline will see their shoot density half in less than a decade. In fact, since 2000, some (Pollença Bay, Mallorca; La Fossa, Alicante) have already lost 40% of their shoot density.

These results show that most Spanish coastal seagrass meadows have been declining over the present decade. The rate of decline of *P. oceanica* meadows is currently 5% per year, slightly lower than that of corals—the marine ecosystem undergoing the fastest decline—and higher than the global loss rate of marshes and mangrove forests (Duarte et al. 2008). This places *P. oceanica* meadows among the most threatened marine ecosystems on the planet. The general decline observed recently in Spanish coastal seagrass meadows may not have begun so recently, however. A retrospective demographic analysis of 27 *P. oceanica* meadows on the Spanish coast showed that 80% of them were already declining between 1967 and 1992 (Marbà et al. 1996). And the scale of their decline in the present decade is similar to in the past. This suggests that, over the last four decades, either (1) the same pressures have continued bearing down on seagrass meadows, or (2) a succession of different pressures have brought about a comparable rate of decline.

2.5. CAUSES OF THE DECLINE IN MEDITERRANEAN SEAGRASS MEADOWS

The current decline of seagrass meadows is due to multiple pressures, principally of anthropogenic origin, that act, frequently simultaneously, on the coastal zone. Most of these pressures also set in train synergistic processes that accelerate the decline when they interact (Duarte 1995). Eutrophication, disturbance of sedimentary dynamics, the mechanical destruction of the coastal area, climatic changes such as global warming, and biological perturbations are the main pressures threatening Spanish coastal seagrass meadows.

2.5.1. Eutrophication

The main cause of seagrass meadow decline is eutrophication of the coastal area. This originates from the discharges of agricultural nutrients and organic matter, waste water from the human population, and aquaculture. Dumping nutrients and organic matter into the sea degrades water quality, principally reducing the amount of light reaching the seagrass meadows. Their survival, like that of all aquatic photosynthetic organisms, is conditioned by the amount of light penetrating the water column. Seagrass meadows grow rooted in the sediment, and have their photosynthetic structures (leaves) on the seabed. They thus exhibit the greatest light requirements of all marine photosynthetic organisms (Duarte 1995). The leaves of marine angiosperms absorb three times as much light as do phytoplankton, but the light they absorb per unit weight and their photosynthetic capacity are considerably less (Duarte 1995; Enríquez et al. 1996). In addition, they require far more light to grow than the phytoplankton, because of the high respiration rate needed to maintain their non-photosynthetic parts (roots and rhizomes) (Duarte 1995). Seagrass meadows require environments that receive at least 11% of the surface irradiation in order to survive, while other benthic marine photosynthetic organisms, like corals and macroalgae, can grow on seabeds that receive only 0.02% or 0.0005% respectively (Gattuso et al. 2006). The position of seagrass meadows in the water column and their high demand for light make them extremely vulnerable to any deterioration of water transparency (Duarte 1995). Nutrient supply stimulates the proliferation of phytoplankton in the water column and of macroalgae on the seagrass meadow's foliar canopy. The proliferation of both groups of organisms reduces the amount of light that the seagrass meadows receive. Seagrass meadows are most vulnerable to increased water turbidity at their depth limit, and this close relationship allows us to develop predictive models for their lower depth limit based on rates of light extinction in the water column (Duarte et al. 2007; figure 2.3), and therefore to predict the magnitude of meadow depletion as water transparency diminishes.

Eutrophication also causes excessive sediment enrichment by nutrients and organic matter. *P. oceanica* meadows are very sensitive to deteriorating sediment quality, and their decline accelerates when the amounts of organic matter and phosphorus reaching the sediment exceed 1-2 g dry weight m^{-2} d^{-1} and 0.04 g P m^{-2} d^{-1} respectively (Díaz-Almela et al. 2008b). The excess nutrients and organic matter in the sediment stimulate bacterial activity, and consequently increase anoxia and the production and concentration of hydrogen sulfide. When the concentration of hydrogen sulfide in the sediment is high and that of oxygen in the plant is low, the hydrogen sulfide in the interstitial water penetrates the seagrass tissues and damages their meristems, thereby reducing their growth and survival (Borum et al. 2005). Hydrogen sulfide

Figure 2.3: Relationship between maximum colonization depth of seagrass meadows of different species and the light extinction coefficient

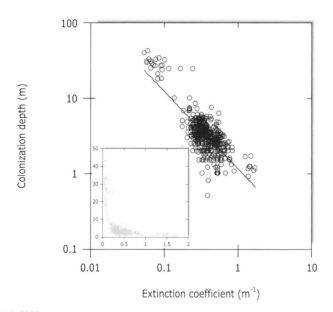

Source: Duarte et al. 2007.

toxicity may be attenuated by the presence of labile iron in the sediment, which can remove hydrogen sulfide from the interstitial water, precipitating it in the form of iron sulfides. Sediments in which little iron is available—a characteristic of the carbonate-rich sediments (Berner 1984) common throughout the Mediterranean—have a very limited capacity to attenuate the toxicity of hydrogen sulfide, making seagrasses more vulnerable to their organic enrichment. In the Balearic Islands, where the labile iron content of sediments is extremely low (Holmer, Duarte, and Marbà 2003), the state of seagrass meadows is conditioned by the supply of iron from external sources. The risk of decline in *P. oceanica* meadows increases when they receive less than 43 mg Fe m^{-2} d^{-1} (Marbà et al. 2008). Moreover, *P. oceanica* meadows are acutely sensitive to hydrogen sulfide. While many species of marine angiosperms can grow and survive in sediments with hydrogen sulfide concentrations up to 100 µM (Terrados et al. 1999), *P. oceanica* meadows decline more rapidly when its concentration in the interstitial water is greater than 10 µM (Calleja, Marbà, and Duarte 2007; figure 2.4). Once sediments have become contaminated it is very difficult for them to recover, and *P. oceanica* meadows continue to decline for years after the input of organic matter has ceased (Delgado et al. 1999).

Figure 2.4: Relationship between the net growth rate of the population of *P. oceanica* shoots in seagrass meadows and the concentration of hydrogen sulfide in the sediment. Negative net population growth rates represent rates of decline. The dotted line indicates the threshold concentration of hydrogen sulfide above which a meadow's decline is significant.

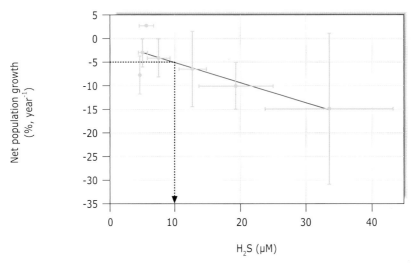

Source: Calleja, Marbà, and Duarte 2007.

2.5.2. Alteration of coastal sediment balance and mechanical perturbations

The disruption of the sediment balance in the coastal area increases the mortality of seagrass shoots. *P. oceanica* shoots have their meristems on the sediment surface, and their survival depends on maintaining that position throughout their life. *P. oceanica* meadows can survive burial rates of up to 4-5 cm year^{-1}, on account of the growth of their vertical rhizomes (Manzanera, Pérez, and Romero 1998). When sediment deposition exceeds this threshold, meadow decline accelerates, and depositions of 14 cm produce 100% shoot mortality. Sediment erosion is another cause of greater shoot mortality.

The transformation of our coastline due to the runaway construction of buildings and seafronts and the damming of rivers diminishes sediment supply to seagrass meadows. In the last 50 years, the amount of sediment reaching the Mediterranean coast has fallen by 90%, and a large part of the area is suffering erosion (Benoit and Comeau 2005). Coastal constructions like breakwaters and ports destroy the adjoining marine communities and can alter local sediment dynamics, increasing erosion and deposition of sediments in some zones. Dredging works on the seabed near seagrass meadows can easily destroy areas of meadow by directly pulling up fragments or eroding or burying them. These impacts principally affect the upper limit of seagrass meadows. Indeed recent studies show that some *P. oceanica* meadows have retreated 25 meters in 20 years (Besterrechea et al., unpublished results).

Trawling is an important cause of large-scale seagrass meadow destruction, with deep communities the worst affected. Trawling with nets above meadows tears out the shoots and rhizomes at rates between 100,000 and 360,000 per hour^{-1} (González-Correa et al. 2005), while at the same time resuspending sediment and increasing water turbidity. The slow seagrass meadow recolonization rate means that the impact of trawling can persist for decades (González-Correa et al. 2005).

In coastal areas that receive large numbers of visitors, the anchoring of pleasure craft above seagrass meadows causes a significant reduction in shoot density. It is estimated that an average of 34 shoots anchor^{-1} (Francour et al. 1999) are torn up during an anchoring cycle (lock-in and retrieval).

2.5.3. Rising sea temperature

Recent studies indicate that *P. oceanica* meadows are vulnerable to Mediterranean warming. Surface water temperature increased by 0.04°C year^{-1} between 1980 and 2006 (Díaz-Almela et al. 2007a), and the highest value recorded was in summer 2003. Global warming affects biological processes like reproduction and may alter the stability of plant communities (e.g., Parmesan and Yohe 2003).

In the last 40 years, it has been observed that the number of *P. oceanica* meadows that flower each year and their flowering intensity (the fraction of a meadow's shoots that flower) vary interannually, with reproductive peaks every 9-11 years (Díaz-Almela, Marbà, and Duarte 2007a). Temporal fluctuations in seagrass meadow reproduction are coupled with sea temperature variations, such that reproduction increases as the temperature climbs. In autumn 2003, one month after the warmest recorded surface temperature in the Mediterranean of the last four decades, there was an episode of mass flowering throughout the western Mediterranean that extended to over 90% of seagrass meadows, representing a flowering intensity twice as high on average as during earlier reproduction peaks (Díaz-Almela, Marbà, and Duarte 2007a; photos 2.10 and 2.11). The relation between increased flowering of seagrass meadows and Mediterranean warming might reflect the plant's response to thermal stress, as occurs in some terrestrial plant communities (e.g., Peñuelas et al. 2002).

Photo 2.10: Seagrass meadow with inflorescences

Photo 2.11: Raft of *P. oceanica* fruits floating on the sea after the mass flowering episode of 2003

The mortality rate of *P. oceanica* meadows has varied interannually in the last seven years, with the highest shoot mortality recorded after very hot summers (Díaz-Almela et al., in review). This annual variability is related to sea water temperature, whereby the mortality rate rises 3% per year[-1] for each degree of increase in maximum annual temperature (Marbà et al., unpublished results). These observations also suggest that *P. oceanica* meadows may decline more rapidly when Mediterranean warming produces temperatures in excess of 28°C, since above this threshold the birth rate through clonal growth and sexual reproduction (Díaz-Almela et al., in review) is insufficient to compensate for the increased death rate (Marbà et al., unpublished results).

The greater mortality of *P. oceanica* meadows as a result of the warming occurring in the Mediterranean Sea may not only reflect the effect of temperature on the plant's physiology. The rise in sea temperature may stimulate other biological processes in the ecosystem, such as community respiration and microbial activity in sediments, which, acting synergistically, could hasten their decline.

2.5.4. Biological invasions

An increased number of marine species are growing beyond their original biogeographic distribution limits (Williams 2007). Some introduced species settle and behave as invasive species, causing a deterioration of native habitats. Maritime traffic, aquaculture, and the opening of sea-to-sea canals like the Suez Canal are the main vectors of species introduction (e.g., Gollasch 2005). The Mediterranean has the greatest number of exotic species of all European seas and the fastest rate of introductions in the whole of Europe. It is estimated to have 662 exotic taxa, of which 325 can be considered established, while the rate of introduction of new species has been reckoned at one every six weeks since the year 1950. This rate, moreover, has been accelerating since the late 1990s, mainly as a result of increased introductions of benthic macroalgal species (Gollasch 2005). Currently, the Mediterranean is home to around 100 species of introduced macroalgae, six of which live in seagrass meadows (Williams 2007), and 10% of which exhibit invasive behavior (Ballesteros, Cebrián, and Alcoverro 2007).

The impact of biological invasions on seagrass meadow stability has been examined for some species of invasive macroalgae. The best-studied of these exotic species are the macroalgae *Caulerpa taxifolia* and *C. racemosa* (photos 2.12 and 2.13). *C. taxifolia* was introduced into the Mediterranean from the Monaco aquarium in 1984, while *C. racemosa* var. *turbinata-uvifera*, originally from the Red Sea, was introduced in the 1920s, and *C. racemosa* var. *cylindracea*, which comes from Australia, was introduced in the 1990s. Both species are clonal green algae, can grow on *P. oceanica* rhizomes and sediment, and are between six and ten times smaller than its leaves. *Caulerpa* species accordingly find it hard to compete for light with *P. oceanica* and do not seem to penetrate dense and healthy seagrass meadows. However, these species grow in organic matter-rich sediments with high hydrogen sulfide concentrations and stimulate the rate of sulfate reduction in the colonized sediment. The proliferation of *Caulerpa* species in seagrass meadows could degrade sediment quality (Holmer et al., in press) and, in conjunction with other disruptions (e.g., eutrophication, Chisholm et al. 1997), accelerate seagrass decline.

In the last decade, the red macroalga *Lophocladia lallemandii*, which originates from the Indo-Pacific and entered the Mediterranean Sea through the Suez Canal, has rapidly invaded western Mediterranean seagrass meadows. Its development is seasonal, and it grows forming patches on the leaves and rhizomes of *P. oceanica* (photo 2.14). The proliferation of *L. lallemandii* in seagrass meadows increases shoot mortality and halves the density and size of surviving *P. oceanica* shoots in comparison to non-invaded areas (Ballesteros, Cebrián, and Alcoverro 2007). The amount of light that *P. oceanica* receives during the invasion of *L. lallemandii* is probably insufficient to sustain its metabolic balance.

The red macroalga *Acrothamnion preissii*, a species native to the Indo-Pacific region and observed in the Mediterranean since 1969 (Williams 2007), is another invader of *P. oceanica* meadows. Invasion by this species does not seem to alter meadow stability, but it displaces most of the epiphytic macroalgae on plant rhizomes, reducing species diversity and habitat complexity (Piazzi and Cinelli 2003).

2.5.5. Pathogenic organisms

Although microorganisms abound in the ocean (e.g., 10^6 bacteria cells ml^{-1} and 10^7 virus particles ml^{-1}; Fuhrman 1999; Marie et al. 1999; Azam and Worden 2004), little information exists about their role as agents potentially pathogenic to marine plants. However, there is evidence of massive seagrass meadow mortality caused by pathogenic marine organisms. The decline of *Zostera*

Photo 2.12: The alga *Caulerpa taxifolia* growing in a *P. oceanica* meadow

Photo 2.13: *Caulerpa racemosa* growing on a community of native macroalgae in Portals Vells, Mallorca

Photo 2.14: Sponge (*Sarcotragus foetidus*) between a *Posidonia oceanica* bed and the invasive alga *Lophocladia lallemandi*. Cala Galiota, Cabrera, Balearic Islands.

marina and *Thalassia testudinum* meadows respectively along the Atlantic coast (1930s) and in Florida Bay (1980s) is associated with infection by marine protists of the genus *Labyrinthula* (Muehlstein et al. 1988; Robblee et al. 1991), when these act in combination with other environmental factors causing meadow deterioration (e.g., temperature increase, hypoxia, raised concentration of hydrogen sulfide in the sediment).

Recent studies have shown the presence in *P. oceanica* tissues of bacteria of the genera *Vibrio*, *Marinomonas*, and *Pseudoalteromonas*, and of the protist *Labyrinthula* (Marco-Noales et al. 2006; Vergeer and Den Hartog 1994). *Pseudoalteromonas* spp. bacteria are more abundant in seagrass meadows with high shoot mortality rates, which suggests that they may be contributing to *P. oceanica*'s decline (Marco-Noales et al. 2006). *Labyrinthula* is a widely distributed organism in Spanish coastal seagrass meadows and is observed in more than 70% of those bordering the Balearic coast (18 meadows examined in total, Garcias-Bonet et al. 2008). Experiments infecting healthy *P. oceanica* shoots with different *Labyrinthula* strains suggest that the virulence of this protist varies from one strain to another. However, the majority (71%) of those tested are capable of producing lesions in *P. oceanica*'s leaves (Garcias-Bonet et al. 2008). Although the presence of pathogenic organisms has not been shown to increase seagrass meadow mortality in the Mediterranean, they could increase the risk of ecosystem decline under conditions of environmental deterioration.

2.6. THE FUTURE OF SEAGRASS MEADOWS

The general decline affecting Mediterranean seagrass meadows is the result of isolated impacts that are hard to pin down, deriving from human population growth along the coast and on a global scale. Currently 40% of the Mediterranean coastline is built-up area. In 2000, it had more than 400 million residents, 70 million of them living in cities of over 100,000 inhabitants, and visitor numbers exceeding 200 million (Benoit and Comeau 2005). Predictions of human population growth suggest that by 2025, 50% of the coast will be built-up area, Mediterranean coastal cities with more than 100,000 inhabitants will be home to 90 million residents, and the coastal strip will receive more than 300 million tourists (Benoit and Comeau 2005). Not only that, aquacultural production in the Mediterranean is expected to double in the next 25 years, maritime freight traffic to almost quadruple, and passenger traffic to likewise double (Benoit and Comeau 2005). Assuming this scale of growth of

Photo 2.15: *P. oceanica* **meadow near Tabarca Island, Alicante, Spain**

human activity, the risk of deterioration of the coastal area, as exemplified by problems of eutrophication, erosion, proliferation of invasive species, and seabed destruction, and, therefore, the risk of seagrass meadow decline, can only increase in the years to come.

The climate change augured for the 21st century, arising from the increased concentration of greenhouse gases in the atmosphere, is a further threat to seagrass meadow conservation. The climate change scenarios managed by the IPPC point to an increase in sea level of between 0.09 and 0.88 m between 1990 and 2100 and an increase of 4°C in the temperature of the Mediterranean (IPPC 2001). Such a rise in sea level would cause coastal erosion and, therefore, hasten the decline of seagrass meadows' upper limit. According to the predictions of climatic warming and *P. oceanica*'s sensitivity to sea temperature increases, the seagrass meadow mortality rate could be three times its current level by 2100. Although the increased temperature would also stimulate sexual reproduction, and thus the formation of new clones, this would not be enough to offset death losses of meadows, so the rate of decline could well accelerate.

Reversing the trend of decline in seagrass meadows and conserving them in future will call for the implementation of management measures to minimize the deterioration of coastal areas. We currently have a European, national, and regional legal framework that, effectively implemented, would facilitate conservation of *P. oceanica* meadows. The European Union, through Agenda 21, requires member states to protect up to 12.2% of their entire territory, which in Mediterranean countries with long coastlines is largely made up of *P. oceanica* meadows, and its fishing regulations prohibit trawling on seagrass meadows (Regulation (EC) 1626/94). Likewise, the EU Habitat Directive (Council Directive 92/43 of May 21, 1992) sets forth measures to guarantee biodiversity through the conservation of natural habitats, including seagrass meadows. In Spain, some autonomous communities, such as Valencia and Catalonia, also have regulations in place to protect seagrass meadows, and the Law of Coasts regulates the protection and use of the coastal area. However, measures to control the dumping of urban, industrial, and aquacultural waste in the Mediterranean Sea have still to be fully enforced: in 2002, 60% of urban waste water was still being dumped into the sea untreated, particularly in its south and eastern reaches (Benoit and Comeau 2005). Since 1997, the Mediterranean Action Plan under the direction of UNEP, with 16 countries affiliated, has included a protocol on pollution from land-based sources and a strategic plan to combat it. The European Union's Water Framework Directive, in force since 2000, defines a set of ambitious objectives to protect the quality of European water bodies, including those of the coasts. The United Nations Framework Convention on Climate Change, known as the Kyoto Protocol, has the goal of stabilizing greenhouse gas emissions at a level that impedes anthropogenic interference in the climate system.

But the conservation of seagrass meadows, their functions, and the services they provide does not just depend on an effective legal framework. It also requires advances in scientific knowledge, the development of technologies to reverse the decline and mitigate impacts, more social awareness around environmental issues, and coordinated action on a global scale. Only with the collaboration of science, technology, the legislator and society at large will it be possible to preserve these millennia-old and immensely valuable Mediterranean ecosystems.

ACKNOWLEDGEMENTS

This chapter summarizes some of the results obtained and discussions held by the *Praderas* project's team of over twenty researchers, coordinated by Carlos M. Duarte. I am also grateful to Elena Díaz-Almela for her comments and contributions, which have helped improve the quality of the text.

REFERENCES

ARNAUD-HAOND, S., C. M. DUARTE, E. DIAZ-ALMELA, N. MARBÀ, and E. A. SERRÃO. "Extant Pleistocene clones detected in a threatened seagrass: some ecological and evolutionary implications of extreme life span potential in clonal organisms." *BMC Evolutionary Biology* (in review).

AZAM, F., and A. Z. WORDEN. "Microbes, molecules, and marine ecosystems." *Science* 303 (2004): 1622-1624.

BALLESTEROS, E., E. CEBRIÁN, and T. ALCOVERRO. "Mortality of shoots of *Posidonia oceanica* following meadow invasion by the red alga *Lophocladia lallemandii.*" *Botanica Marina* 50 (2007): 8-13.

BARRÓN, C., C. M. DUARTE, M. FRANKIGNOULLE, and A. VIEIRA BORGES. "Organic carbon metabolism and carbonate dynamics in a Mediterranean seagrass (*Posidonia oceanica*) meadow." *Estuaries and Coasts* 29 (2006): 417-426.

BENOIT, G., and A. COMEAU. *A Sustainable Future for the Mediterranean: the Blue Plan's Environment and Development Outlook*. London: Earthscan, 2005.

BERNER R. A. "Sedimentary pyrite formation: An update." *Geochimica et Cosmochimica Acta* 48 (1984): 605–615.

BORUM, J., O. PEDERSEN, T. M. GREVE, T. A. FRANKOVICH, J. C. ZIEMAN, J. W. FOURQUREAN, and C. J. MADDEN. "The potential role of plant oxygen and sulphide dynamics in die-off events of the tropical seagrass, *Thalassia testudinum.*" *Journal of Ecology* 93 (2005): 148-158.

CALLEJA, M., N. MARBÀ, and C. M. DUARTE. "The relationship between seagrass (*Posidonia oceanica)* decline and porewater sulfide pools in carbonate sediments." *Estuarine, Coastal and Shelf Science* 73 (2007): 583-588.

CHISHOLM, J. R. M., F. E. FRENEX, D. MATIEU, and J. M. JAUBERT. "Wastewater discharge, seagrass decline and algal proliferation on the Côte d'Azur." *Marine Pollution Bulletin* 34 (1997): 78-84.

DELGADO, O., J. RUIZ, M. PÉREZ, J. ROMERO, and E. BALLESTEROS. "Effects of fish farming on seagrass (*Posidonia oceanica*) in a Mediterranean bay: seagrass decline after organic loading cessation." *Oceanologia Acta* 22 (1999): 109-117.

DIAZ-ALMELA, E., N. MARBÀ, and C. M. DUARTE. "Fingerprints of Mediterranean Sea warming in seagrass (*Posidonia oceanica)* flowering records." *Global Change Biology* 13 (2007a): 224-235.

DÍAZ-ALMELA, E., S. ARNAUD-HAOND, M. S. VLIET, E. ALVAREZ, N. MARBÀ, C. M. DUARTE, and E.A. SERRAO. "Feed-backs between genetic structure and perturbation-driven decline in seagrass (*Posidonia oceanica*) meadows." *Conservation Genetics* 8 (2007b): 1377-1391.

DÍAZ-ALMELA, E., N. MARBÀ, E. ÁLVAREZ, R. SANTIAGO, R. MARTÍNEZ, and C. M. DUARTE. "Patch dynamics of the Mediterranean seagrass *Posidonia oceanica*: Implications for recolonisation process." *Aquatic Botany* 89 (4) (2008a): 397-403.

DÍAZ-ALMELA, E., N. MARBÀ, E. ÁLVAREZ, R. SANTIAGO, M. HOLMER, A. GRAU, S. MIRTO, et al. "Benthic input rates predict seagrass (*Posidonia oceanica*) fish farm-induced decline." *Marine Pollution Bulletin* 56 (7) (2008b): 1332-1342.

DUARTE, C. M. "Allometric scaling of seagrass form and productivity." *Marine Ecology Progress Series* 77 (1991): 289-300.

DUARTE, C. M. "Submerged aquatic vegetation in relation to different nutrient regimes." *Ophelia* 41 (1995): 87-112.

DUARTE, C. M., and C. L. CHISCANO. "Seagrass biomass and production: a reassessment." *Aquatic Botany* 65 (1999): 159-174.

DUARTE, C. M., W. C. DENNISON, R. J. W. ORTH, and T. J. B. CARRUTHERS. "The charisma of coastal ecosystems." *Estuaries and Coasts* (2008): doi 10.1007/s12237-008-9038-7.

DUARTE, C. M., N. MARBÀ, D. KRAUS-JENSEN, and M. SÁNCHEZ-CAMACHO. "Testing the predictive power of seagrass depth limit models." *Estuaries and Coasts* 30 (2007): 652-656.

DUARTE, C. M., J. J. MIDDELBURG and N. CARACO. "Major role of marine vegetation on the oceanic carbon cycle." *Biogeosciences* 2 (2005): 1-8.

ENRÍQUEZ, S., C. M. DUARTE, K. SAND-JENSEN, and S. L. NIELSEN. "Broad scale comparison of photosynthetic rates across phototrophic organisms." *Oecologia* 108 (1996): 197-206.

FRANCOUR, F., A. GANTEAUME, and M. POULAIN. "Effects of boat anchoring in *Posidonia oceanica* seagrass beds in the Port-Cros National Park (north-western Mediterranean Sea)." *Aquatic Conservation: Marine and Freshwater Ecosystems* 9 (1999): 391-400.

FUHRMAN, J. A. "Marine viruses and their biogeochemical and ecological effects." *Nature* 399 (1999): 541-548.

GARCIAS-BONET, N., T. D. SHERMAN, C. M. DUARTE, and N. MARBÀ. "*Labyrinthula* in Western Mediterranean seagrass (*Posidonia oceanica*) meadows: biogeography and pathogenicity." 2008 Ocean Sciences Conference, Orlando.

GATTUSO, J.-P., B. GENTILI, C. M. DUARTE, J. A. KLEYPAS, J. J. MIDDELBURG, and D. ANTOINE. "Light availability in the coastal ocean: impact on the distribution of benthic photosynthetic organisms and their contribution to primary production." *Biogeosciences* 3 (2006): 489-513.

GAZEAU, F., C. DUARTE, J.-P. GATTUSO, C. BARRÓN, N. NAVARRO, S. RUIZ, Y. T. PRAIRIE, et al. "Whole-system metabolism and CO_2 fluxes in a Mediterranean Bay dominated by seagrass beds (Palma Bay, NW Mediterranean)." *Biogeosciences* 2 (2005): 43-60.

GIBBS, A., and A. MACKENZIE. "A primer pair for amplifying part of the genome of all potyvirids by RT-PCR." *Journal of Virological Methods* 63 (1997): 9-16.

GOLLASCH, S. "Overview on introduced aquatic species in European navigational and adjacent waters." *Helgoland Marine Research* 60 (2005): 84-89.

GONZÁLEZ-CORREA, J. M., J. T. BAYLE, J. L. SÁNCHEZ-LIZASO, C. VALLE, P. SÁNCHEZ-JEREZ, and J. M. RUIZ. "Recovery of deep *Posidonia oceanica* meadows degraded by trawling." *Journal of Experimental Marine Biology and Ecology* 320 (2005): 65-76.

HENDRIKS, I. E., T. SINTES, T. J. BOUMA, and C. M. DUARTE. "Experimental assessment and modeling evaluation of the effects of the seagrass *Posidonia oceanica* on flow and particle trapping." *Marine Ecology Progress Series* 356 (2008): 163-173.

HOLMER, M., C. M. DUARTE, and N. MARBÀ. "Sulfur cycling and seagrass (*Posidonia oceanica*) status in carbonate sediments." *Biogeochemistry* 66 (2003): 223-239.

HOLMER, M., N. MARBÀ, M. LAMOTE, and C. M. DUARTE. "Deterioration of sediment quality in seagrass meadows *(Posidonia oceanica)* invaded by macroalgae *(Caulerpa* sp.)." *Estuaries and Coasts* (in press).

IPPC (Intergovernmental Panel on Climate Change). *Climate Change 2001. Third Assessment Report of the Intergovernmental Panel on Climate Change*. Cambridge: Cambridge University Press, 2001.

KENDRICK, G., N. MARBÀ, and C. M. DUARTE. "Modelling formation of complex topography by the seagrass *Posidonia oceanica*." *Estuarine Coastal and Shelf Science* 65 (2005): 717-725.

LARKUM, A. W. D., R. J. ORTH, and C. M. DUARTE, eds. "*Seagrasses: Biology, Ecology and Conservation*." Dordrecht: Springer (2006).

MANZANERA, M., M. PÉREZ, and J. ROMERO. "Seagrass mortality due to oversedimentation: an experimental approach." *Journal of Coastal Conservation* 4 (1998): 67-70.

MARBÀ, N., and C. M. DUARTE. "Rhizome elongation and seagrass clonal growth." *Marine Ecology Progress Series* 174 (1998): 269-280.

MARBÀ, N., C. M. DUARTE, J. CEBRIAN, M. E. GALLEGOS, B. OLESEN, and K. SAND-JENSEN. "Growth and population dynamics of *Posidonia oceanica* on the Spanish Mediterranean coast: elucidating seagrass decline." *Marine Ecology Progress Series* 137 (1996): 203-213.

MARBÀ, N., C. M. DUARTE, E. DÍAZ-ALMELA, J. TERRADOS, E. ÁLVAREZ, R. MARTÍNEZ, R. SANTIAGO, et al. "Direct evidence of imbalanced seagrass (*Posidonia oceanica*) shoot population dynamics along the Spanish Mediterranean." *Estuaries* 28 (2005): 51-60.

MARBÀ, N., C. M. DUARTE, M. HOLMER, M. L. CALLEJA, E. ÁLVAREZ, E. DÍAZ-ALMELA, and N. GARCIAS-BONET. "Sedimentary iron inputs stimulate seagrass (*Posidonia oceanica*) population growth in carbonate sediments." *Estuarine, Coastal and Shelf Science* 76 (2008): 710-713.

MARCO-NOALES, E., M. ORDAX, A. DELGADO, M. M. LÓPEZ, M. J. SAAVEDRA, A. MARTÍNEZ-MURCIA, N. GARCIAS, et al. "Microbiota associated with *Posidonia oceanica* in Western Mediterranean sea." In A. Mendez-Vilas, ed. *Modern Multidisciplinary Applied Microbiology: exploiting microbes and their interactions*. Weinheim: Wiley-VCH, 2006. 114-119.

MARIE D., C. P. D. BRUSSAARD, R. THYRHAUG, G. BRATBAK, and D. VAULOT. "Enumeration of marine viruses in culture and natural samples by flow cytometry." *Applied and Environmental Microbiology* 65 (1999): 45-52.

MATEO, M. A., J. ROMERO, M. PÉREZ, M. M. LITTLER, and D. S. LITTLER. "Dynamics of millenary organic deposits resulting from the growth of the Mediterranean seagrass *Posidonia oceanica*." *Estuarine Coastal and Shelf Science* 44 (1997): 103-110.

MUEHLSTEIN, L. K., D. PORTER, and F. T. SHORT. "*Labyrinthula* Sp, a marine slime-mold producing the symptoms of wasting disease in eelgrass, *Zostera marina*." *Marine Biology* 99 (1988): 465-472.

PARMESAN, C., and G. YOHE. "A globally coherent fingerprint of climate change impacts across natural systems." *Nature* 421 (2003): 37-42.

PEÑUELAS, J., I. FILELLA, and P. COMAS. "Changed plant and animal life cycles from 1952 to 2000 in the Mediterranean region." *Global Change Biology* 8 (2002): 531-544.

PIAZZI, L., and F. CINELLI. "Evaluation of benthic macroalgal invasion in a harbour area of the western Mediterranean." *European Journal of Phycology* 38 (2003): 223-231.

ROBBLEE, M. B., T. R. BARBER, P. R. CARLSON, M. J. DURAKO, J. W. FOURQUREAN, L. K. MUEHLSTEIN, D. PORTER, et. al. "Mass mortality of the tropical seagrass *Thalassia testudinum* in Florida Bay (USA)." *Marine Ecology Progress Series* 71 (1991): 297-299.

ROZENFELD, A. F., S. ARNAUD-HAOND, E. HERNÁNDEZ-GARCÍA, V. M. EGUÍLUZ, M. A. MATÍAS, E. SERRAO, and C. M. DUARTE. "Spectrum of genetic diversity and networks of clonal organisms." *Journal of the Royal Society Interface* 4 (2007): 1093-1102.

SHORT, F. T., and C. M. DUARTE. "Methods for the measurement of seagrass growth and reproduction." In F. T. Short and R. G. Coles, eds. *Global Seagrass Research Methods.* Amsterdam: Elsevier Science B.V., 2001. 155-182.

SINTES, T., N. MARBÀ, and C. M. DUARTE. "Modeling non-linear seagrass clonal growth: Assessing the efficiency of space occupation across the seagrass flora." *Estuaries and Coasts* 29 (2006): 72-80.

TERRADOS, J., C. M. DUARTE, L. KAMP-NIELSEN, J. BORUM, N. S. R. AGAWIN, M. D. FORTES, E. GACIA, et al. "Are seagrass growth and survival affected by reducing conditions in the sediment?." *Aquatic Botany* 65 (1999): 175-197.

VERGEER, L. H. T., and C. DENHARTOG. "Omnipresence of Labyrinthulaceae in seagrasses." *Aquatic Botany* 48 (1994): 1-20.

WILLIAMS, S. L. "Introduced species in seagrass ecosystems: Status and concerns." *Journal of Experimental Marine Biology and Ecology* 350 (2007): 89-110.

3. GLOBAL TRAJECTORIES OF SEAGRASSES, THE BIOLOGICAL SENTINELS OF COASTAL ECOSYSTEMS

William C. Dennison
University of Maryland Center for Environmental Science
United States

Stretch'd on her mossy couch, in trackless deeps,
Queen of the coral groves, **Zostera** *sleeps;*
The silvery sea-weed matted round her bed,
And distant surges murmuring o'er her head.—-
High in the flood her azure dome ascends,
The crystal arch on crystal columns bends;
Roof'd with translucent shell the turrets blaze,
And far in ocean dart their colour'd rays;
O'er the white floor successive shadows move,
As rise and break the ruffled waves above.—-
Around the nymph her mermaid-trains repair,
And wave with orient pearl her radiant hair;
With rapid fins she cleaves the watery way,
Shoots like a silver meteor up to day;
Sounds a loud conch, convokes a scaly band,
Her sea-born lovers, and ascends the strand.

An excerpt from Erasmus Darwin "The Botanic Garden.
A Poem, in Two Parts." Part II. "The Loves of the Plants" (1791)

3.1. INTRODUCTION

Seagrasses are unique flowering plants that live totally submersed in shallow coastal seas. They are distributed along coastlines of tropical and temperate oceans and are particularly sensitive to changes in water quality. The ecological services that seagrasses provide include nutrient absorption, carbon sequestration, nursery and habitat for fish and shellfish, food for several threatened species, sediment stabilization, and water clarity improvements. Seagrasses have not received as much research attention as other coastal habi-

◀ **Photo 3.1: A prairie of the seagrass *Cymodocea nodosa* in the Mediterranean Sea**

91

tats and, more significantly still, have received only a fraction of the media attention. As a result of their sensitivity to water quality and their global coastal distributions, seagrasses make excellent biological sentinels of the health of coastal ecosystems. Reports of seagrass losses (and gains) over the past 127 years have been published, but a quantitative assessment of their trajectories has been lacking until very recently. A global seagrass trajectories database was established and analyzed, and seagrass declines were identified in the majority of reports (58%), with no change or small increases identified in the remaining reports. More concerning was that the rate of seagrass decreases was accelerating. Global losses of seagrass area since 1980 are equivalent to a football (soccer) field every 30 minutes, using a very conservative estimate. However, accounts of small-scale seagrass recoveries illustrate that water quality improvements can go some way to reversing the damage. The quantitative assessment of seagrass trajectories leads us to conclude that coastal ecosystems are being impacted at a global scale, and seagrasses are particularly at risk. To preserve seagrasses and their ecological services, there is a critical need for a targeted global conservation effort.

3.2. SEAGRASSES ARE UNIQUE

Seagrasses are flowering plants that live completely submersed in shallow coastal seas. They live alongside various algae, including red, brown and green algae ("seaweed"), but are evolutionarily very different from algae. Marine algae have evolved in the ocean over billions of years and are evolutionarily very primitive, but seagrasses have evolved from land plants over the past 100 million years. Seagrasses are the only terrestrial plants to fully recolonize the sea; a surprising development considering that all plant life originated in the marine environment. It is interesting that there are no marine mosses, ferns or conifers, and only flowering plants have been able to recolonize the sea. Salt marsh plants and mangrove trees are flowering plants that also evolved from land plants, but they are restricted to the intertidal zone. There are only about 60 species of seagrasses in the world—these species live completely submersed, up to 50 or more meters deep. This stands in contrast to the 100,000 species of terrestrial flowering plants in the world. In spite of the low species diversity, these 60 seagrass species have been incredibly successful at colonizing vast stretches of coastline, forming extensive meadows and playing important ecological roles in coastal marine ecosystems. We can find analogies here to some marine mammals; whales and dolphins evolved from land animals, are few in species but are found in all oceans and have important ecological functions.

Photo 3.2: Leaves of the seagrass *Posidonia oceanica* waving in the water currents

The term "seagrass" does not connote that these specialized plants are a true grass. Rather it is a descriptive term, since the long strap-like leaves of most seagrass species wave in the currents like a field of grass in the wind. Also, the evolutionary analysis of the origin of seagrasses indicates multiple, separate lines of evolutionary lineage, so the term "seagrass" is not a taxonomic grouping of closely related plants, but a functional grouping of plants that look and act similarly (Hemminga and Duarte 2003). In some cases, seagrasses can look quite similar to "seaweeds"; green marine algae that may live alongside them. The various environmental factors that influence both seagrasses and seaweeds can result in similar growth forms and functions, in spite of their very different lineages. There are some freshwater flowering plants that look and act like seagrasses, and some freshwater species can actually survive in the slightly salty water found in estuaries. But the term "seagrass" is restricted to those species of flowering plants that can live totally submersed in full strength seawater.

Seagrasses have colonized the shallow coastal waters throughout tropical and temperate oceans (Larkum, Orth, and Duarte 2006). They have adapted to their completely submersed life with a series of fascinating adaptations. For example, seagrasses have evolved complex pollination mechanisms involving mass spawning and the longest pollen grains in the plant kingdom. They also have internal gas canals that inflate by day and deflate by night, with internal winds to transport oxygen to their underground roots. Seagrasses have their chloroplasts in the outermost cells of the leaves, facilitating gas exchange and light acquisition. Their fiber-filled, strap-like leaves can withstand waves and currents that could destroy piers and docks.

Seagrass roots exude dissolved organic matter into the surrounding sediments, which stimulates various microbes, including nitrogen-fixing bacteria. These nitrogen-fixing bacteria absorb nitrogen gas dissolved in the pore water of sediments and convert it to ammonia, which is biologically available for other organisms. Tracer studies have revealed that nitrogen gas can be converted into ammonium by bacteria, released and taken up by seagrass roots, and transported to seagrass leaves within the short span of several hours. This relationship between seagrasses and microbes in the microzones around seagrass roots is analogous to the symbiotic bacteria within the roots of terrestrial plants, for example, the legumes. This seagrass/microbe quasi-symbiosis comes into play with regard to dugong grazing. Not all seagrasses are the same

Photo 3.3: A dugong (*Dugong dugon*) grazing on a tropical seagrass meadow

with regard to their degree of root exudation and associated nitrogen fixation. It turns out that the seagrass species that are most preferred by dugong also have the most active root microbes. Moreover, the dugong-preferred species have seeds that can pass through dugong guts and remain viable. In this way, continual dugong grazing can maintain a population of seagrasses which rejuvenate their nutrients through nitrogen-fixing microbes. This intimate relationship between dugong and seagrasses has likely developed through co-evolution over millennia.

3.3. SEAGRASSES ARE WIDESPREAD GLOBALLY

Seagrasses uniquely have *both* tropical and temperate distributions (Green and Short 2003). Coral reefs and mangrove forests are largely restricted to tropical regions, while salt marshes and kelp forests tend to be confined to temperate regions. Perhaps due to their multiple evolutionary lineages into the sea from multiple terrestrial progenitors, there are different assemblages of temperate and tropical seagrasses. Seagrasses have been found growing under sea ice along the Alaskan coast at temperatures of less than 0°C, as well as in shallow tropical lagoons at temperatures in excess of 40°C. Seagrasses grow along the coastlines of every continent except Antarctica.

In some areas of the world, extensive shallow water habitats support extensive seagrass meadows (Short et al. 2007). The most significant of these extensive meadows in terms of area and species diversity is in southwest Australia (Carruthers et al. 2007). Not unlike what northeast Australia's Great Barrier Reef is for corals, the southwest Australian coastline has a series of limestone reefs extending for 2,500 km, which provide habitat for vast seagrass meadows containing a third of the global seagrass species. Southwest Australia has unique oceanographic features, including a warm ocean current that flows along the coast during winter, counter to the oceanic gyre circulation pattern. This unique oceanographic feature, as well as the chain of offshore limestone reefs, makes this coastline Australia's second Great Barrier Reef. There are various other areas that have extensive seagrass meadows, including some between the coral reefs of the Great Barrier Reef. In fact, the area of the Great Barrier Reef Marine Park covered by hard corals (6%) is less than that covered by seagrasses (13%). The ratio of reef to seagrass area is even more skewed in the Florida Bay/Florida Keys and reef tract, where the hard coral area (5%) is considerably less than the seagrass area (95%).

3.4. SEAGRASSES PROVIDE KEY ECOLOGICAL SERVICES

Tropical seagrasses are food for several threatened species, including manatees in the Atlantic Ocean, dugong in the Indian and Pacific oceans and green sea turtles globally. These megaherbivores graze seagrass meadows repeatedly, and they have been called "cultivation grazers". Due to historical overharvesting of these megaherbivores, the species composition and ecological role of seagrass meadows in some regions have been dramatically affected (e.g., throughout the Caribbean). Temperate seagrasses are food for waterfowl, particularly black brant geese. Sea urchins in both tropical and temperate regions feed on seagrasses, and they are part of the diets of various fish, particularly gar and pinfish. Although only a select number of animals feed on them directly, a multitude of organisms, plant and animal, depend on seagrasses as habitat for part or all of their life cycles (Heck et al. 2008). Epiphytes that live attached to seagrass leaves or stems form a teeming microscopic ecosystem of productive plants and animals. A variety of clams, oysters, scallops, and other filter feeders live on and in seagrass meadows. Various juvenile fishes use them as a protective nursery to avoid predation, while other species like seahorses live a cryptic life among their swaying leaf canopies.

The way that seagrasses cope with fouling by epiphytic organisms is to constantly shed old leaves and grow new ones. A healthy seagrass shoot produces new leaves at the rate of one every 7-10 days. With shoot densities of hundreds to thousands of shoots per square meter, this means that seagrass meadows are virtually factories of what becomes detritus. The fate of this detritus is important ecologically to adjacent ecosystems. Seagrass detritus is often washed up on beaches, and it is possible to see piles of this wrack over three meters high stretching for kilometers. Human use of seagrass wrack has included housing insulation, mattress stuffing, roof thatching and automobile seat stuffing (including the original Volkswagens). Seagrass beach wrack leaches nutrients into salt marshes and coastal waters and supports amphipods and other small animals. In the ocean, meantime, seagrass detritus is decomposed by bacteria and other microorganisms. These microbes then support a detritus food web that ultimately depends on seagrass. Seagrass also gets washed into the deep sea, littering the seafloor and collecting in deep trenches where the slow-paced life can slowly decompose it.

Seagrass leaf canopies baffle the water column, reducing water motion within the meadow. This reduction in water motion allows small particles to settle out, falling to the seafloor. Sediments that collect in seagrass meadows are smaller in size than in surrounding unvegetated areas. These small particles are

Photo 3.4: A Mediterranean moray eel (*Muraena helena*) within a prairie of the seagrass *Cymodocea nodosa*

organic-rich, thus baffling by seagrass canopies serves to increase the organic content of their sediments. Organic-rich sediments provide a substrate for bacteria, which decompose the organic material, releasing the locked-up nutrients. Seagrass roots can then absorb these nutrients to support the meadow. As a result, the leaf baffling and subsequent sedimentation in seagrass meadows make seagrass meadows giant "filter feeders", augmenting their diet by extracting nutrients from small particles that were in the water column.

Another important ecological service that seagrasses provide is a result of sediment binding by their below-ground roots and rhizomes. The organic substances released by seagrass roots provide a sticky matrix that helps bind the sediment grains together. Leaf baffling reduces the erosive force of waves and tides that would otherwise resuspend sediments. In this way, seagrass meadows act like a ground cover that keeps the water column clear of resuspended sediments and protects the shore from some of the erosive force of waves and currents.

In our current situation of greenhouse gas accumulations causing climate change, seagrasses have a particularly important role in mitigating carbon dioxide concentrations. Seagrasses evolved into their submersed existence when global carbon dioxide concentrations were higher than they are now, and their photosynthesis has been shown to be stimulated when carbon dioxide concentrations are increased. Since seagrass carbon is often not directly consumed and decomposes slowly, seagrass peat is formed in some regions and, in others, seagrass detritus is transported to the deep sea. These fates serve to effectively remove the carbon, making seagrass an important carbon sink for the planet.

To put some of its ecological services into context, a soccer field of seagrass can absorb 5.8 kg of nitrogen per year (based on *Posidonia* meadow nitrogen uptake rates), equivalent to the treated effluent of 780 people (assuming a per capita rate of sewage production and secondary treatment). The same soccer field of seagrass can absorb 166 g of carbon per meter^2 per year, equivalent to CO_2 emissions from an automobile traveling 12,000 km. The ecological services of seagrasses have been estimated at 32,000 euros/hectare per year (Costanza et al. 1997).

3.5. SEAGRASSES ARE BIOLOGICAL SENTINELS

Seagrasses are "coastal canaries", a reference to their sensitivity to water quality. Miners used to take canaries into mineshafts, because of their lack of tolerance to degraded air quality. If the canary fainted or died, the miners knew to act swiftly and decisively and vacate the mineshaft immediately, leaving diagnosis and corrective action for a later date. Seagrasses are intolerant of water quality reductions; in fact, seagrass minimum light requirements are uniquely high among all plants. In general, seagrasses need 10-35% of ambient sunlight to simply survive and appreciably more to thrive (Duarte et al. 2007). This high minimum light requirement makes them particularly sensitive to water clarity reductions, just as the canaries were sensitive to air quality. When sediments or nutrients from land wash into the ocean and directly or indirectly lead to light reductions, seagrasses will be the first to respond. They have proven to be good biological indicators of water quality, with the result that seagrass monitoring programs have been instituted in locations as diverse as the Mediterranean Sea, Great Barrier Reef, Chesapeake Bay and Florida Bay.

Seagrasses have the ability to tap the rich nutrient resources within the soft sediments of shallow coastal seas. Their roots can absorb the dissolved nutrients, while xylem and phloem transport them internally. But nutrient-rich sediments also present a challenge to plant life, since the processes that produce these nutrients also produces a potentially toxic environment. Oxygen is consumed faster than it can diffuse from the overlying water, and toxic compounds like hydrogen sulfide accumulate. Seagrasses counter toxic compounds like sulfide by transporting oxygen from leaf photosynthesis in internal air canals (lacunae) to their roots. The additional oxygen needed for this detoxification of sediments results in seagrasses requiring higher quantities of light than other marine plants, making them particularly vulnerable to light reductions.

Light reductions can occur in the water column due to dissolved substances, suspended sediments and phytoplankton. Also, epiphytes or sediment particles on seagrass leaves can further reduce the light reaching plants. Some seagrasses develop significant sugar and starch reserves to withstand temporary dips in light, but chronic light reductions through eutrophication or increased suspended sediments lead eventually to their demise. There are also other environmental factors that cause seagrass loss, among them introduced species, burial or erosion, storm damage and boat or fishing damage, but it is their sensitivity to light reductions that accounts for the most massive and persistent losses.

3.6. SEAGRASSES ARE THREATENED

Seagrass losses have been documented for over a century. A growing body of knowledge on seagrass declines stimulated a recent quantitative global assessment (Waycott et al., in review). The magnitude of global seagrass loss rates was determined by assembling a global scientific team, devising and populating a database of published seagrass assessments and analyzing this database. Although the scientific team was familiar with seagrass dynamics and had been documenting losses in their respective regions, the fact that seagrass declines were so pervasive globally was a revelation. What they found was a global rate of decline in the seagrass area of -0.9% year^{-1} (median rate) and -1.5% year^{-1} (mean rate), using published seagrass trajectories from 216 meadows spanning 127 years. Of particular concern is that the rate of decline is quickening, with the overall median rate (-3.7% year^{-1}) accelerating as far as -5.5 to -8.0% year^{-1} since 1980 in meadows exhibiting loss of area. These published accounts of seagrass losses represent 29% of the global seagrass area since 1980. This high rate of decline and loss places seagrass meadows among the most threatened habitats on Earth, and reveals a major environmental crisis in coastal oceans.

The number of seagrass meadows with increasing, no change and decreasing trajectories increases every decade, revealing the intensified sampling effort of recent years. The predominance of decreasing trajectories is evident, and the increase in all three trajectory categories is projected to continue through the rest of the current decade. The μ value, rate of change, has varied with time, and the largest rates, both positive and negative, occur in recent rather than older data sets. In addition to the three trajectory categories, records were kept over a decade of seagrass meadows that were either absolute gains (newly created) or losses (extinctions), with 10 out of 216 meadows qualifying. Area changes over time were particularly marked in the 1980s and 1990s, driven mainly by a large-scale decline in the northwest Florida panhandle region (United States) over the period 1984-1992.

Global seagrass loss rates since 1980 are equivalent to losing a soccer field every 30 minutes, day and night, every single day. This means that in the time it takes to play a soccer match, three fields of seagrass have disappeared. A troubling aspect about this calculation is that it is extremely conservative. For example, published seagrass assessments only account for a small fraction (9%) of the mapped seagrass area. Thus it is most likely that a soccer field of seagrass area is lost every three minutes or perhaps at even shorter intervals, since the mapped seagrass area is a fraction of its actual extent. The lack of good estimates of global seagrass area is because seagrasses are notoriously difficult to assess, confounding both remote sensing efforts and field surveys when they are in murky or deep water, remote regions of the world or growing cryptically and mixed with other features. The known global seagrass area is certainly an underestimate, with the potential area up to 35 times higher. That we have a globally significant problem is clear enough, but its actual magnitude remains elusive, and a global effort is required to assess the real seagrass area.

3.7. SEAGRASSES HAVE A "CHARISMA GAP"

In spite of their widespread distribution and important ecological role, the public perception of seagrasses has lagged behind that of other coastal ecosystems (Duarte et al. 2008). This was recently documented in a comparison of seagrass, salt marsh, mangrove and coral scientific publication rates and media accounts. The scientific publication rates of coral reefs exceeded those of salt marshes, mangroves and seagrasses, with corals having roughly 4 times the annual rate of seagrasses. Media accounts were likewise highest in coral reefs, followed by salt marshes and mangroves, with seagrasses in the rear. Coral reefs had roughly 40 times more media reports than seagrasses. For every coral

Photo 3.5: Seahorses make their home in seagrass prairies worldwide

reef scientific publication, there were over 130 media reports, whereas for every seagrass scientific publication there were fewer than thirteen. This disconnect between scientific and public awareness needs to be addressed in the light of the important ecological role of seagrasses and the global declines being reported.

Seagrasses are not inherently "sexy" to the casual observer, lacking the colorful fish of coral reefs or the showy flowers of terrestrial plants. The animals that live within seagrass meadows are often cryptic or microscopic. Seagrass pollination is not via animals that are attracted to flowers, so colorful petals are not required. To appreciate the life within seagrass meadows, instead of swimming over the swaying leaves, divers need to settle into the canopy and wait patiently for animals to lose their fear and come slowly out to investigate. Seahorses, eels, crabs, lobsters, flounder, tiny gobies, snails, sea squirts, and other creatures will begin to move about. In tropical regions, manatees or dugong will uproot entire plants like a farmer's plow, and turtles will snip off leaves like a lawn mower, but these shy animals will generally avoid divers.

In order to overcome this "charisma gap", seagrasses need to have better press agents. Over a billion people live within 50 km of a seagrass meadow, far more than live near coral reefs or mangrove forests, yet only a miniscule fraction of these billion people even know seagrasses exist. Of course they often live in environments hostile for humans, with large waves and currents, turbid or deep water, large predators, animals that sting, bite or stab, and uncomfortable water temperatures. And they are frequently found in remote or hard-to-access locations. These factors make visits to seagrass meadows difficult and serve to limit the number of people that experience them first hand. Maintaining seagrasses in an aquarium is possible, but not easy, which further reduces their familiarity to the non-diving public. Hence the "charisma gap" and the need for seagrass scientists, who invariably become conservation advocates, to provide the public with more seagrass images, videos and information.

3.8. A GLOBAL SEAGRASS CONSERVATION EFFORT IS NEEDED

While the overall situation of global seagrass declines is rather bleak, there are some encouraging case studies of seagrass recoveries that need to be studied and ultimately emulated widely. The seagrass recovery in Tampa Bay, Florida has been linked to sewage treatment upgrades. These and other case studies provide an impetus to reduce sewage effluents and other nutrient sources into coastal waters.

Photo 3.6: Extensive seagrass prairies or meadows form when there is adequate light reaching soft sediments

Various seagrass restoration attempts around the world have shown us, firstly, that seagrass transplanting is labor intensive and expensive, and, secondly, that its long-term success is marginal at best. In cases where environmental degradation has led to seagrass losses, simply initiating transplanting or reseeding schemes will not work, unless the causes of the original degradation have been reversed. An important caveat regarding seagrass recovery efforts is where seagrass distributions are limited by available propagules (e.g., the Virginia coastal bays program by Bob Orth and colleagues). The important lesson from seagrass restoration efforts is that prevention of environmental degradation is a far more cost effective and successful management strategy than the restoration of degraded ecosystems.

What can an individual do on behalf of seagrasses? There are, in fact, a variety of activities that will aid in seagrass conservation. Citizens monitoring programs for seagrasses and associated water quality have been set up in some areas with the involvement of non-scientists. The non-governmental organizations that support marine conservation have not, to date, embraced seagrass conservation, focusing instead on more charismatic ecosystems (e.g., tropical rain forests, coral reefs) or megafauna (e.g., whales, pandas). As shareholders in these NGOs, citizens can help direct activities toward seagrass conservation. An often overlooked aspect of any conservation activity is to actually visit a seagrass meadow. Spending time in and among seagrasses is an expression of caring and can help raise awareness. Eating seafood caught or raised in an environmentally friendly manner is another way to help, since fish pens and aquaculture ponds have been shown to have deleterious impacts on seagrasses.

For coastal residents, a responsible attitude to seagrass is particularly important. Boat propeller scars can destroy seagrass beds, and responsible sailing is a prime requirement, as is taking care not to transport plants or animals from one water body to another, to avoid introductions of exotic species. Houses along the coast should have nutrient removal septic systems for the treatment of sewage. Basically, anything a coastal resident can do to minimize their impact on nutrient and sediment runoff will benefit seagrasses. The hardening of shorelines by coastal development may provide some temporary relief for coastal erosion in the face of a sea level increase, but a hardened shoreline will prevent seagrasses from migrating inshore as the sea level rises.

Climate change impacts have recently been receiving considerable global attention. Basically, recommendations to reduce the carbon footprint for greenhouse gases will have positive benefits for seagrasses. While elevated carbon dioxide levels might aid them physiologically, the overall ecological effect of climate change would be detrimental to seagrasses. Several recent cases of temperature stress have led to seagrass declines. Changes in rainfall patterns, in which extended dry periods are punctuated by intense rainfall, increase delivery of sediments and nutrients, again with a harmful effect on seagrass meadows.

Marine conservation is just now embracing protected (no-take) areas analogous to refuges and parks in terrestrial ecosystems. Approximately 11% of the land surface is protected, whereas marine protected areas make up less than 1%. Most marine protected areas are designed for fisheries management and for habitats like coral reefs. Incorporating seagrasses into the design criteria and operation of marine protected areas is strongly recommended.

The important ecological role of seagrasses and the recent reports of their global decline provide a strong impetus to develop a global seagrass conservation effort (Orth et al. 2006). If we see seagrasses as coastal canaries providing an early warning for coastal ecosystem degradation, we should follow the lead of the miners when their mineshaft canaries lost consciousness or died. They did not debate the cause(s) of the damage—they acted swiftly and decisively by first removing themselves from danger and then working to resolve the problem. And we must also react swiftly and decisively to the warning of our seagrass canaries. This action could go as far as a moratorium on coastal development, pending appropriate mitigation efforts to avoid further environmental degradation of coastal ecosystems. While there are a multitude of causes of seagrass declines, the common thread is human coastal development. What is needed then is to reduce our human footprint on the coastal zone as a matter of urgency, so future generations can enjoy seagrasses and healthy coastal ecosystems.

ACKNOWLEDGEMENTS

My colleagues on the Seagrass Trajectories Working Group, an initiative sponsored by the National Center for Ecological Analysis and Synthesis were essential for the development of the concepts and data expressed in this chapter. This group, comprising Ainsley Calladine, Tim Carruthers, Carlos Duarte, Jim Fourqurean, Ken Heck, Randall Hughes, Gary Kendrick, Jud Kenworthy, Suzanne Olyarnik, Bob Orth, Fred Short, Michelle Waycott, and Susan Williams also reviewed the manuscript and made helpful suggestions. This is contribution number 4290 of the University of Maryland Center for Environmental Science.

REFERENCES

CARRUTHERS, T. J. B., W. C. DENNISON, G. A. KENDRICK, M. WAYCOTT, D. I. WALKER, and M. L. CAMBRIDGE. "Seagrasses of south-west Australia: A conceptual synthesis of the world's most diverse and extensive seagrass meadows." *Journal of Experimental Biology and Ecology* 350 (2007): 21-45.

COSTANZA, R., R. D'ARGE, R. DE GROOT, S. FARBER, M. GRASSO, B. HANNON, K. LIMBURG, et al. "The value of the world's ecosystem services and natural capital." *Nature* 387 (1997): 253-260.

DUARTE, C. M., W. C. DENNISON, R. J. ORTH, and T. J. B. CARRUTHERS. "The charisma of coastal ecosystems: Addressing the imbalance." *Estuaries and Coasts* 31 (2008): 233-238.

DUARTE, C. M., N. MARBÀ, D. KRAUSE-JENSEN, and M. SANCHEZ-CAMACHO. "Testing the predictive power of seagrass depth limit models." *Estuaries and Coasts* 30 (2007): 652-654.

GREEN, E. P., and F. T. SHORT, eds. *World Atlas of Seagrasses: Present Status and Future Conservation.* Berkeley: University of California Press, 2003.

HECK, K. L., JR., T. J. B. CARRUTHERS, C. M. DUARTE, A. R. HUGHES, G. A. KENDRICK, R. J. ORTH, and S. L. WILLIAMS. "Trophic transfers from seagrass meadows subsidize diverse marine and terrestrial consumers." *Ecosystems* 11 (2008): 1198-1210.

HEMMINGA, M., and C. M. DUARTE. *Seagrass Ecology.* Cambridge: Cambridge University Press, 2000.

LARKUM, A. W. D., R. J. ORTH, and C. M. DUARTE, eds. *Seagrasses: Biology, Ecology and Conservation.* Dordrecht: Springer, 2006.

ORTH, R. J., T. J. B. CARRUTHERS, W. C. DENNISON, C. M. DUARTE, J. W. FOURQUREAN, K. L. HECK, JR., A. R. HUGHES, et al. "A global crisis for seagrass ecosystems." *Bioscience* 56 (2006): 987-996.

SHORT, F. T., T. J. B. CARRUTHERS, W. C. DENNISON, and M. WAYCOTT. "Global seagrass distribution and diversity." *Journal of Experimental Biology and Ecology* 350 (2007): 3-20.

WAYCOTT, M., C. M. DUARTE, T. J. B. CARRUTHERS, R. J. ORTH, W. C. DENNISON, S. OLYARNIK, A. CALLADINE, et al. "Accelerating loss of seagrasses across the globe threatens coastal ecosystems." *Proceedings of the National Academy of Sciences* (in review).

4. GLOBAL LOSSES OF MANGROVES AND SALT MARSHES

Ivan Valiela[1], Erin Kinney[1], Jennifer Culbertson[2], Emily Peacock[3], and Stephen Smith[4]

[1] Marine Biological Laboratory, The Ecosystems Center, Woods Hole, MA, United States
[2] Department of Biology and Marine Biology, University of North Carolina, Wilmington, NC, United States
[3] Woods Hole Oceanographic Institution, Woods Hole, MA, United States
[4] Cape Cod National Seashore, National Park Service, Wellfleet, MA, United States

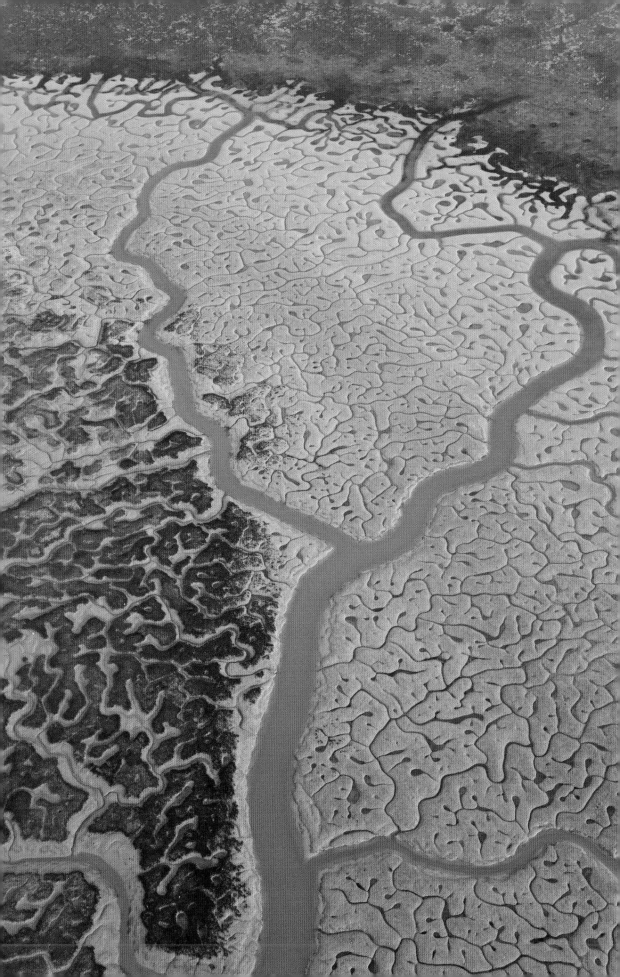

4.1. INTRODUCTION

THE WORLD'S ENVIRONMENTS are undergoing remarkable changes, and the rate of change appears to be accelerating. Perhaps we are simply more aware of such alterations, but the reality is that if we measure almost any environmental quantity today, change is taking place, often at surprising rates. There is little doubt as to the root causes underlying the ever more evident environmental alterations: human-related influences far outweigh variations owing to sidereal or geological forcings (Valiela 2006).

The powerful anthropogenic changes derive basically from the unprecedented rise in human numbers through the 20th century, from perhaps 1.5 billion people to about 6 billion in 2000. Human populations are forecast to increase by another 30% or so by 2050. Of course, the demands for energy, food, water, and other resources have increased disproportionately in certain regions of the world, and such life-style disparities have added social, economic, and political complications. The importance of rising human numbers and the effects of uneven consumption are well known (Food and Agriculture Organization, http://www.fao.org; Population Reference Bureau, http://www.prb.org; United Nations, http://www.un.org/popin/wdtrends.html). Perhaps less common is awareness of two other aspects that are relevant to the loss of coastal wetlands, the topic of this contribution.

First, we are at a momentous stage in human history: we have just passed the point where fully 50% of us live in urbanized settings (Food and Agriculture Organization, http://www.fao.org). The proliferation of urban areas is unmistakably evident in an enhanced nocturnal composite image taken from orbit (photo 4.2). Humans living in aggregated fashion make greater demands on resources, consume proportionately greater amounts of energy (because of the

◀ **Photo 4.1: Salt marshes form complex networks of tidal channels.** Water circulates during the tidal cycle and small topographic differences result in important changes in vegetation and biodiversity.

Photo 4.2: Europe from orbit. Mosaic of enhanced nocturnal images of Europe taken from orbit.
Source: http://www.gsfc.nasa.gov/topstony/2003/0815citylights.html.

extra demand for transportation of goods and people, heating and cooling, water supply, and so on), as well as occupying what might previously have been productive agricultural areas with valuable soils (Dow and DeWalle 2000; Van Breemen et al. 2002). In certain parts of the world, rather large proportions of the land have been urbanized (table 4.1). Expanding urban areas also eliminate natural areas that provide ecological subsidies such as nutrient retention and atmospheric cooling, and in general intensify issues of disposal

Table 4.1: Percentage of the area of states in four U.S. regions converted to urban sprawl; defined as "wildland-urban interface", the area where residences intermingle with native vegetation.

States located on the	% area of the state converted to the wildland-urban interface
Atlantic coast	38.6
Gulf of Mexico coast	10.8
Pacific coast	6.5
Interior	3.6

Source: Data from Radeloff et al. 2005.

of waste water, solid waste, industrial effluents, and vehicular and commercial exhausts. All in all, urbanization of landscapes presses intensification of all environmental management issues. As it turns out, major cities of the world have developed at critical transport nexus, often estuaries. Environments in the interface between land and sea—mangroves and salt marshes prominent among them—have therefore borne much of the brunt of urbanization.

Second, human beings have a propensity to accumulate near shore, as is also evident in the nocturnal image of the European region (photo 4.2). Regardless of the spatial scale—global (figure 4.1.A) or local (figure 4.1.B)—we build

Figure 4.1.A: Estimated number of people at different distances from the shore, worldwide

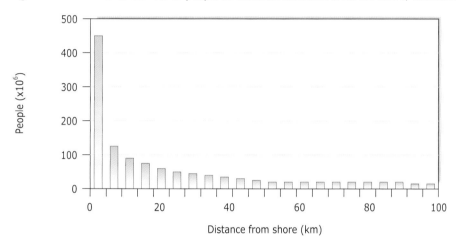

Figure 4.1.B: **Estimated number of buildings at different distances from the shore, in Waquoit Bay**, a small, local estuarine system in Cape Cod, MA, United States.

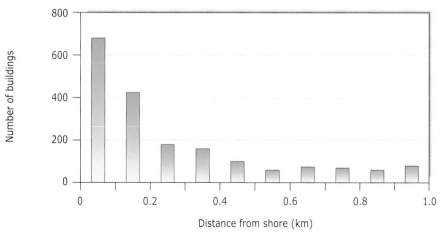

Source: Adapted from Valiela 2006.

structures as near to water as seems possible. This fractal tendency exacerbates the effects of increasing urbanization. Whatever the impacts of more people in denser population centers, coastal environments seem likely to suffer greater pressures. In the U.S., for example, the greatest degree of urban sprawl has taken place in coastal areas of the Atlantic and Gulf of Mexico (table 4.1), which happen to be where the majority of the coastal wetlands are found.

Coastal mangroves and salt marshes—along with most other coastal wetland environments—have to some degree been altered by changes brought about by increasing human activity. There are large discrepancies from place to place, but, globally, there have been substantial losses in area of both habitats, as well as degradation of considerable parts of surviving salt marshes and mangroves.

4.2. THE MAGNITUDE OF WETLAND LOSSES

Historically, wetlands were considered bad places for people, daunting environments where a person would be exposed to unhealthful miasmas. The term "malaria" referred to the bad airs thought to emanate from wet places where one might catch a fatal disease. There is, of course, some truth to such concerns, and the adversarial view is reflected in many different ways: we often refer to "reclamation" of mangroves and marshes, a term which implicitly suggests that by draining and filling we might bring these habitats back to a better state. People saw, and in many places on earth, still see few reasons for the preservation of marshes or mangroves. Wholesale filling, diking, draining, and conversion for agricultural and residential purposes have been the historical consequence of increased population densities near wetland-fringed estuaries, whether in the North Sea, Mondego River, Bangkok, Puerto Rico, Bangladesh, Iraq, Ebro Delta, Llobregat Delta, Boston Harbor, Hackensack River, or outer Cape Cod.

Speculation varies as to the worldwide fate of coastal wetlands. Nicholls et al. (1999) used modeling approaches to calculate losses in the range of 13-31%, of which 0-2% would plausibly be related to sea level rise. More recently, the IPCC (2007) issued a somewhat more pessimistic estimate of about a 30% loss of coastal wetlands worldwide. These are educated guesses, based on incomplete data. What we can be sure of is that future losses of coastal wetlands are inexorable, and that most losses will be directly or indirectly linked to human activity. In the sections that follow, we discuss the specific situations of mangrove forests and salt marshes.

4.2.1. Magnitude of mangrove forest losses

There has been much professional and press interest in the substantial ecological changes taking place in tropical latitudes. Such interest was the result of reports that about 30% of the area of global tropical forests, including rainforests, would be lost by the year 2000 (IPCC 1996). As regards coral reefs, alarms are being raised about a 10% loss of the habitat area, with perhaps an additional 30% degraded by midway through the 20th century (Wilkinson 1999); these statistics do not include the coral bleaching experienced worldwide late in the century (Baker et al. 2008). From such reports, we can safely conclude that there have been considerable recent alterations to significant habitats in the tropics.

The loss of area has been even more marked in the case of mangrove forests. From a meta-analysis of available data, we found that globally about 35% of the area of mangrove forests has disappeared since 1980 (Valiela, Bowen, and York 2001a). The loss of mangrove area averages about 2.1% per year, with greater annual losses of up to 3.6% per year in the Americas (table 4.2). Such estimates are confirmed by regional studies (Honculada-Primavera 1995; Blasco, Aizpuru, and Gers 2001). High recent loss rates make mangrove forests the most threatened major coastal habitat in the world.

Photo 4.3: Mangrove forests grow along the intertidal area of tropical and subtropical deltas.
Glades like these support important ecosystem functions.

Table 4.2: Current mangrove swamp areas, percent loss, annual loss rate, and percent of original area lost per year, for the mangroves of the continents and the world

	Current mangrove area (km^2)	% loss of mangrove forest area	Annual rate of loss (km^2 y^{-1})	% of original area lost per year
Asia	77,169	36	628	1.52
Africa	36,529	32	274	1.25
Australasia	10,287	14	231	1.99
Americas	43,161	38	2,251	3.62
World	166,876	35	2,834	2.07

Source: Data from Valiela et al. 2001.

4.2.2. Magnitude of salt marsh losses

There are regional-scale assessments of salt marsh areas affected by human pressure. San Francisco Bay has seen a 79% reduction in area of salt marshes (figure 4.2), as well as a 9.932% increase in human-altered or constructed habitats (lagoons, salt ponds, etc.) (table 4.3). Some restoration efforts are underway to re-create native environments in South San Francisco Bay. In Chesapeake and Delaware bays, U.S., 10-20% were near lost in 1993 (table 4.4). There are some regional reconstructions of historical trajectories: about 50% of the salt marsh area in New England had been lost by the mid-1970s (figure 4.3). More recently, salt marsh loss rates have remained low in the U.S. (table 4.5), because of public awareness of the importance of these habitats, in particular the role of the main salt marsh grass in the region, the cordgrass *Spartina alterniflora*, and the ensuing enacting of restrictive protective legislation (Valiela 2006; Bromberg and Bertness 2005).

Figure 4.2: Changes in salt marsh area around San Francisco Bay, California. Dark blue represents salt marsh.

Table 4.3: Conversion of coastal wetland habitats in San Francisco Bay, across nearly two centuries, from natural systems to human-dominated land covers

Environments	% change
Native aquatic habitats:	
Open bay water	−7
Tidal flats	−42
Tidal marsh	−79
Human-dominated aquatic habitats:	
Lagoons	4,209
Salt ponds	2,062
Other altered areas	58,179
Total human-dominated aquatic habitats	9,932
Native coastal land habitats	−74

Source: Valiela 2006.

Table 4.4: Condition of estuarine marsh areas in Chesapeake and Delaware bays, 1993

	Condition (as % of the area of wetland)		
	Non-degraded	Slightly to moderately degraded	Severely to completely degraded
Chesapeake Bay	28-31	50-52	19-20
Delaware Bay	38-55	35-43	10-19

Source: Data from Kearney et al. 2002.

Table 4.5: Losses of coastal wetlands in the co-terminous U.S., 1920s-1980s

Years	% loss	% y⁻¹
1922-1954	6.5	0.2
1950s-1970s	-	_1
1970s-1980s	1.7	0.15
1975-1985	1.1	0.11
1982-1987	1.1	0.18

1 Annual losses were higher in certain places, such as coastal Louisiana, where rates reached 0.86 per year during 1958-1974.
Source: Adapted from data compiled from numerous sources (Valiela, Bowen, and York 2006).

Figure 4.3: Time course of area of salt marsh within states of the New England region, United States

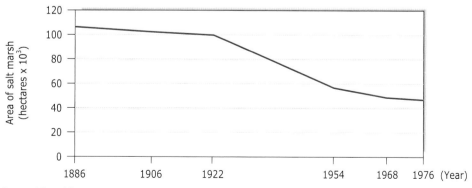

Source: Adapted from Nixon 1982.

115

4.3. THE CAUSES OF WETLAND LOSSES

4.3.1. Salt marshes

4.3.1.1. LOSSES FROM CONSTRUCTION PROJECTS

By and large, in the United States at least, salt marsh losses before the 1970s were caused by some type of construction or civil engineering project. Coastal wetlands were, for one purpose or another, filled with imported sediment, drained of water, and diked to separate the wetland from tidal influences. The losses reported in tables 4.3-4.5 are largely a result of this sort of direct human intervention. It is no surprise, therefore, that reduction of salt marsh habitats was historically associated with increased urbanization of the adjoining watersheds (figure 4.4).

4.3.1.2. LOSSES FROM SEA LEVEL RISE

In certain places within the U.S. and other countries, evidence that salt marshes furnished important ecological and economic services useful to people led to laws being passed during the second half of the 20th century that restricted our historical imperative—and apparent license—to "reclaim" such land. These laws were later extended to cover the protection of mangroves. Hence the recent causes of loss of coastal wetlands are seldom filling, draining, and diking. Of course, there may be no such laws in many other parts of the

Figure 4.4: Loss of salt marsh area relative to increase in urbanized land area in southern New England, United States. Urban growth expressed as square root transformation of the values.

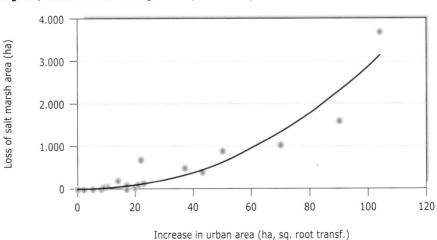

Source: Adapted from Bromberg and Bertness 2005.

Figure 4.5: Annual mean sea level for six Pacific stations. The straight line through the Honolulu data shows a 15 cm increase per century.

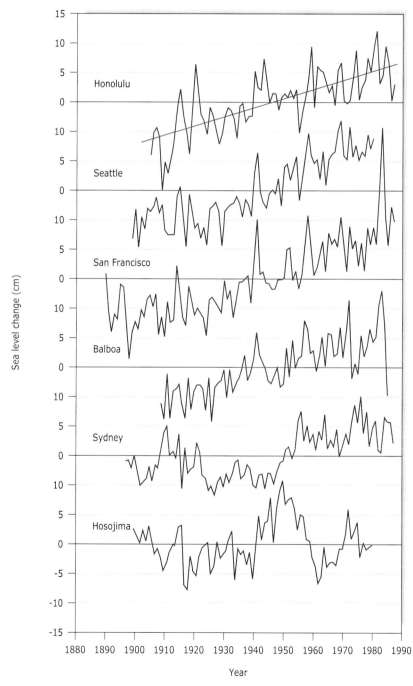

Source: Wyrtki 1990.

world, and the destruction of wetlands may at times take place even in areas under legal protection. In any case, direct human alteration is not currently a major cause of salt marsh and mangrove losses, at least within the U.S. Nonetheless, coastal wetlands are still being lost in the U.S. and the rest of the world. These current and future losses now primarily owe to an indirect result of human activities: increased sea level rise[1].

Sea level has been rising during recent decades across many of the world's shores (figure 4.6), although there is considerable local variation owing to geological processes. As sea level rises, wetland plants must respond, since the species involved are sensitively poised for best survival within certain limits of the tidal range. The physiological restrictions involved in submergence tolerance and redox regimes determine where wetland species will grow best. In general, salt marsh species will retreat landward as sea level rises and, if topography allows, will simultaneously extend further upslope (Wolters et al. 2005). Where salt marshes grow on low-lying islands—as occurs, for example, in many sites along the coast of Virginia (K. McGlathery, pers. comm.) or Maryland (Downs et al. 1994), sea level rise has more drastic effects, as there is no upland to offer a platform for marsh expansion.

Figure 4.6: Tide gauge measurements (m) of 6-month average sea level heights relative to mean high water level, 1932 to 2000

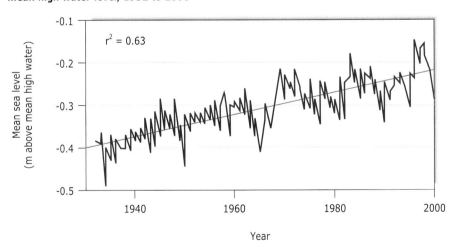

Source: Data from Dr. Richard Paine, Woods Hole Oceanographic Institution (NOAA/NOS).

---

[1] We should note that coastal wetlands have been subject to fluctuations in sea level across geological time. Clear evidence of now submerged coastal wetlands is offered by the chunks of ancient salt marsh peat deposits that are not infrequently caught in bottom trawls towed over the seafloor of Georges Bank (Backus and Bourne 1991); relict mangrove sediments have been found at depth on the shelf of the Great Barrier Reef (Hull 2005).

Photo 4.4: Mangrove forests export carbon and contribute to recruit organisms to the adjacent coastal waters

Across most shorelines, spatial translations, depending on sea level, have been the necessary historical reality for salt marsh vegetation. With the increased urbanization of coastal areas described earlier, there are now people at the landward edge of many wetlands, and they very much prefer to keep marsh vegetation from taking over their land and constructed structures. This dilemma has been referred to as the "coastal squeeze" (Doody 2004), and although the extent of the problem has not been quantified, it may be more common than people realize (Wolters et al. 2005). Sea walls, road (figure 4.7) and rail beds, rip rap, and other erosion-control structures built at the landward edge of wetlands may well prevent the landward movement of salt marsh vegetation, and hence, in the face of sea level rise, lead to reduced salt marsh habitat areas. This possible mechanism of marsh loss needs to be quantified and tested under a variety of sea level rise scenarios.

Salt marshes may have seen the worst of their direct human threats, at least in the countries where protective legislation has been passed. Instead, the salient issue is how this coastal habitat will perform in the face of rising sea levels, and indirect human impact. Here again, urbanization and human construction structures come to bear, as salt marshes might be caught in a "coastal squeeze"

Figure 4.7: Vertical images of two Cape Cod salt marsh sites, taken during 1977-2007 (a) to (f) and (g) to (k). The broken lines show the position of the seaward marsh edge. The edges are composited in (f) and (l) to show the retreat of the marsh across the decades. Note that the marsh site on the left has a road bed on the upland margin which makes it impossible for marsh plants to migrate landward, forcing the loss of salt marsh area.

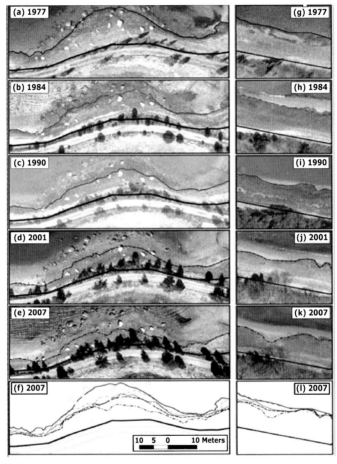

Source: Peacock 2007.

mediated by sea level and erosion-control structures. Assessments are needed of the relative importance of possible salt marsh habitat responses to faster-rising sea levels and the coastal squeeze.

4.3.1.3. LOSSES FROM SALT MARSH DIE-BACK

Recently, another kind of loss of salt marsh habitats has appeared along the east coast of the United States. Die-back describes the near-complete loss of vegetation in salt marsh parcels, with subsequent erosion and down-estuary transport of sediment away from the marsh platform. The lack of marsh plants drastically alters the ability of the habitat to provide the important ecological and biogeochemical services that are described below. Several causes of salt marsh die-back have been suggested. Possible mechanisms include submergence by sea level rise, erosion (Smith, in press), drought, warming, grazing, and fungal infection (Flory and Alber 2002; Alber et al. 2008). Possible causes appear to vary regionally, from drought in Louisiana and Georgia to fungal pathogens in Louisiana and Florida and grazers in parts of Cape Cod and Georgia, and it is likely that multiple control processes also play a part (Alber et al. 2008). In some Cape Cod marshes, grazing by the nocturnal purple marsh crab, *Sesarma reticulatum*, appears to cause low marsh die-back (Holdredge et al., in press; Bertness et al., in press). Due to the close correlation of high marsh die-back with elevation, it is thought that high marsh losses are a result of multiple factors, including herbivory and sea level rise (http://www.nps.gov/caco/naturescience/salt-marsh-dieback.htm; Smith 2008; Smith, in press)

In Georgia, 37 sites were affected by die-back between 2001 and 2003 (Flory and Alber 2002; GCRC 2004; Ogburn and Alber 2006), and the losses have progressed. Die-back has been reported on about 158,000 ha in Louisiana (Callahan and Schneider 2004; McKee, Mendelssohn, and Materne 2004; Edwards, Travis, and Proffitt 2005), and also in New York (Hartig et al. 2002) and South Carolina (J. Morris, unpublished data). In Massachusetts, die-back of salt marsh cordgrass and other plant species (Smith 2006) was reported throughout Cape Cod, and there are new reports from Maine, New Hampshire, New York, and Delaware. Die-back has therefore taken place across a wide range of U.S. coastal stretches. This may be a fairly recent phenomenon in the New World, but older reports describe similar events in European salt marshes (Goodman 1959; Sivanesan and Manners 1970), where die-back apparently came and went in recent decades.

Although the appearance of die-back in the U.S., and Cape Cod in particular, is widespread and losses in select marshes on Cape Cod have been quantified by Smith (in press), we lack enough survey data to determine the full extent of this sort of marsh loss. Loss of creek bank salt marsh plants by die-back may accelerate erosion of the bank habitat (Smith, in press) As yet, die-back affects a minor portion of salt marsh area, but it can be expected to spread further in North America, perhaps later diminishing, as it did after its heyday in Europe.

4.3.1.4. Losses from invasive reed expansion

Another as yet incompletely understood mechanism of salt marsh loss is the relatively recent proliferation of an invasive introduced genotype of the common reed, *Phragmites australis* (http://www.invasiveplants.net/phragmites/morphology.htm; Blossey 2002). The invasive growth usually occurs along the upper edges of salt marshes and extends seaward to increasing degrees. The invasive taxon appears more tolerant of salt (Vazquez et al. 2006), grows better in response to increased nutrients than the native genotype (Packett and Chambers 2006; Saltonstall and Stevenson 2007) and seems to be favored by the urbanization of the adjoining watersheds (King et al. 2007). It has been argued in a long list of papers (see review in Teal and Weistein 2002 and Hunter et al. 2006) that, at least in the U.S. sites, this vegetation type fails to contribute the ecological services (see below) provided by native salt marsh vegetation. Curiously, in China, *Spartina alterniflora* is an invader that is replacing native *P. australis* (Ma et al. 2007), and faunas diminished in invaded areas (Chen et al. 2007). The ongoing reed expansion has been reported widely in North America (Saltonstall 2002). So far there are no comprehensive data on its extent relative to the area of salt marsh, or estimates as to future trends.

Photo 4.5: Reedbeds of common reed (*Phragmites australis*). The common reed can be an aggressive invasive, especially when introduced. Its spread is favored by the urbanization of the areas adjoining salt marshes and its high saline tolerance.

4.3.2. Mangrove forests

4.3.2.1. CONSTRUCTION AND EXPLOITATION EFFECTS

Mangroves have been subject to a variety of human uses, including the harvest of wood for fuel and the production of charcoal, the production of honey, medicinal purposes, and so forth (Saenger 2002). Most of these activities historically did not result in habitat destruction. In recent decades, however, mangrove use has intensified, and substantial loss has become evident (table 4.2, and Valiela et al. 2001b; Alongi 2002; Duke et al. 2007). Mariculture has been prominent among the activities that lead to loss: the construction of shrimp and fish ponds (photo 4.6) accounts for 52% of the world's loss of

Photo 4.6: Bornean mangrove forest. This aerial view shows dykes and enclosed shrimp ponds carved out of the mangrove habitat.

Table 4.6: Recent activities in mangrove forests that have led to loss of habitat

	% of total
Shrimp culture	38
Forestry uses	26
Fish culture	14
Diversion of fresh water	11
Land reclamation	5
Herbicides	3
Agriculture	1
Salt ponds	<1
Coastal development	<1

Source: Adapted from data compiled from numerous sources (Valiela, Bowen, and York 2001).

mangroves. A variety of other construction and exploitation activities add the remainder (table 4.6). The loss from herbicide use occurred during warfare in SE Asia.

4.3.2.2. SEA LEVEL EFFECTS

Sea level rise forces the retreat of the seaward margin of mangroves (Ellison 1993; Field 1995), much as is the case with salt marshes. Across most tropical shores, there is generally less of a built-up urbanized landscape, meaning the mangrove has sufficient space to expand landward (figure 4.8); mangrove sediment sources appear to be enough to support the accretion necessary (Field 1995; Alongi, in press). Different species of mangroves respond differently to experimental exposure to different sea levels (He et al. 2007). These results suggest that we can forecast that increased sea level will not only shift the position of mangrove forests landward, but will also alter the species composition of the forests.

It would be useful to ascertain the extent of the coming coastal squeeze for mangroves, since human populations and the development of urban centers may be increasing faster in low than in high latitudes. Taking the upper limit of the IPCC's sea level rise estimates (IPCC 2007), we might see a loss of 10-15% of current mangrove forest area by the year 2100 (Snedaker 1995; Gill-

Figure 4.8: Changes in the locations of mangrove estuarine habitats and locations of shoreline, 1949 and 1977, Fitzroy River, Australia

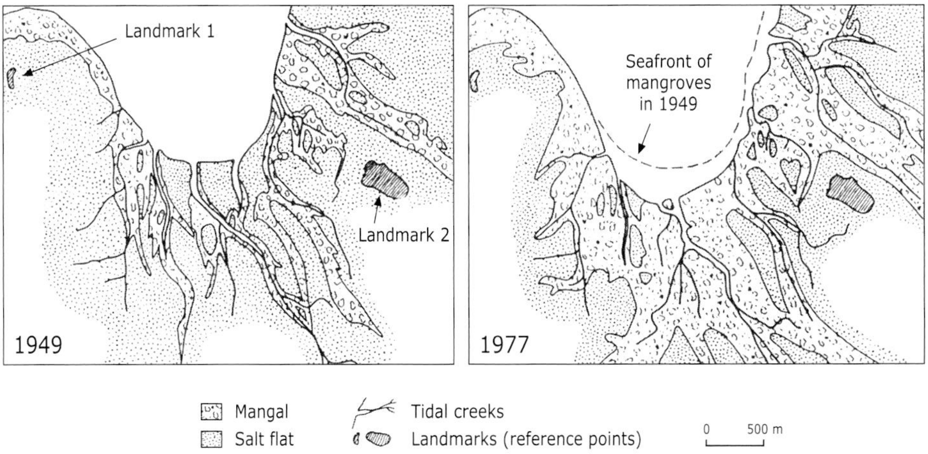

Source: Adapted from Semeniuk 1994.

man et al. 2006). Losses of mangrove forests associated with sea level rise are therefore considerably smaller than the ongoing losses generated by human conversion of mangroves to utilitarian purposes. If estimates of current total losses of 1-2% per year (Valiela, Bowen, and York 2001a; Alongi 2002; Duke et al. 2007) are correct, most of the world's mangroves might have gone before we see the impact of sea level-related losses. This being so, it appears sensible to direct management and restoration efforts toward prevention and remediation of direct mangrove deforestation.

4.4. THE CONSEQUENCES OF COASTAL WETLAND LOSS

So far we have established that, although comprehensive data may be scarce, there is compelling evidence that there have been substantial losses of salt marshes and mangrove forests, two widespread coastal habitats. We can also say that direct and indirect human effects are involved in the substantial ecological changes. The direct effects are via various construction-related activities, and the indirect effects are mediated through our warming of the atmosphere, and hence accelerated sea level rise, added to our possible involvement in other mechanisms. The question that arises at this point is whether or not all that matters.

Photo 4.7: View of a channel in a salt marsh of *Spartina alterniflora* in New Jersey, United States.
The image shows the sharp edges of vegetation and the scattered algal cover often found in the channels.

To address that question, we need to first review the ecological functions played by coastal wetlands as part of the larger coastal zone, including people (Valiela 2006). Services provided by coastal wetlands include the following:

1. *Export of energy-rich materials important to food webs of deeper waters*

Most wetland ecosystems export energy-rich substances (reduced nitrogen compounds, dissolved and particulate organic matter) to adjoining deeper ecosystems (table 4.7). These subsidies can support the high rates of metabolism characteristic of the receiving near-shore waters (Hopkinson 1985). The subsidies in export of energy-containing materials from *Spartina alterniflora* salt marshes to adjoining waters were major arguments supporting the enactment of regulations protecting coastal wetlands in the U.S.

2. *Nurseries to many species of commercially important fisheries stocks*

Many commercially important species of shrimp and fish use wetlands as places where their young find cover and abundant food to support fast growth (Turner 1992; Werme 1981; Twilley 1998; Manson et al. 2005). In eastern North America, for example, menhaden, bluefish, winter flounder, and striped bass are among fish species fundamental to sport and commercial fisheries and are species that also use salt marsh estuaries as juvenile nurseries.

3. *Habitat for shell- and fin-fish stocks*

The rich waters of wetland-dominated estuaries support many commercially important shell- and fin-fish stocks. In temperate North America, for instance, oysters, quahogs, scallops, soft-shell clams, blue crabs, and winter

Table 4.7: Percentage of salt marshes (n=19) exporting materials out to deeper waters

Materials	Percentage of salt marshes studied that exported materials to deeper waters
Ammonium	64
Nitrate	36
Dissolved organic nitrogen	100
Particulate organic nitrogen	67
Total nitrogen	100
Dissolved organic carbon	91
Particulate organic carbon	59
Total carbon	82

Source: Adapted from data compiled from numerous sources (Valiela, Bowen, and York 2001).

Photo 4.8: Prop roots of mangrove trees. The roots form complex structures that serve as habitat for the recruitment of a broad range of species.

flounder—to name a few exploited stocks—are harvested from marsh-fringed estuaries. The values of such harvested crops are typically an order of magnitude larger, on a per unit area basis, than harvests from grains in terrestrial agriculture (Mackenzie 1989; Ver, Mackenzie, and Lerman 1999).

4. *Sites for aquaculture and other uses*

Phytoplankton-rich water within wetland-fringed estuaries are favored sites for mariculture practices, as there is protection from high seas, plentiful food, reasonable water exchanges, and good water quality to support high-density cultivation (Shumway et al. 2003). In Cuba, mangrove oysters are commonly harvested. High densities of suspension feeders may also be useful in clearing water columns, as a tool to improve or restore water quality (Cloern 1982; Ulanowicz and Tuttle 1992).

More intrusive modes of mariculture have been used to convert wetland areas into high-intensity shrimp and fish culture ponds, as noted above in the case of loss of mangrove forest area. In addition, large areas of coastal wetlands have in many places (western Australia, Portugal, San Francisco Bay, to name a few) been diked to create evaporative salt pans for the production of sea salt. Such practices, of course, destroy the wetland involved.

5. *Contaminant interception*

Salt marsh and mangrove sediments to a certain extent retain industrial contaminants, including metals, chlorinated hydrocarbons, and petroleum hydrocarbons (Twilley 1995). The biogeochemical mechanisms involved are complicated, as are the relative responses of the different parts of wetland ecosystems to exposure to these compounds. A summary of recent work in these very large fields of study is provided in Valiela (2006, chaps. 7-9).

6. *Shoreline and sediment stabilization*

The presence of wetland vegetation conserves the stability of coastal sediments in at least two ways. First, marsh or mangrove vegetation dissipates the erosional power of storm waves (Alongi, in press): model studies show that there is a 50% decline in wave energy by 100-150 m into mangrove forests (Brinkman et al. 1997; Mazda, Wolanski, and Ridd 2006), and that there may be a 90% reduction of tsunami flow pressure within 100 m in dense mangrove stands (Harada and Imamura 2005; Tanaka et al. 2007). Such lowering of the motive force of water reduces the transport or erosion of sediments in vegetated wetlands and facilitates trapping of fine sediments within these ecosystems (Perry 2007).

Second, root rhizomes also add coherence to sediments (Alongi 2002). In a site where oil lies some 10-15 cm below the marsh surface, we found that the density of *Spartina alterniflora* shoots was considerable lower than in un-oiled marsh areas (Culbertson et al. 2008). Sediment loss has occurred in oiled sites with decreased plant densities (figure 4.9). Where oil is present, shoot density decreases and the characteristic flat, sloping marsh surface becomes pitted and dissected by gullies.

7. *Sources of forage and hay*

The use of salt marshes as places where livestock forage, or as sources of hay, is a venerable and widespread tradition. Grazing by livestock has been reported to have taken place by about 4000 BC in the Baltic and more recently elsewhere (Adam 2002). Indeed, the practice continues in many places. Visitors to Scotland will see sheep and highland cattle in most marshy areas, while cattle still regularly pasture on marshland in central Argentina and north Queensland. In northern North America, livestock pasturing and the harvest of hay began as early as 1650, and lasted until the late 1900s (figure 4.10). And there is a currently a modest market in marsh hay for horticultural uses.

Figure 4.9: Contours of the surface of salt marsh parcels supporting stands of *Spartina alterni-flora* at higher (A) and lower (B) shoot densities. Note lower elevations on average, and dissected nature of the surface where shoot density was lowered.

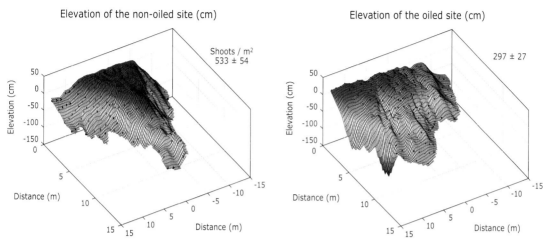

Source: Adapted from Culbertson et al., in press.

Figure 4.10: *Hayfields: a clear day*, painted by Martin Johnson Heade, 1871-1880. This image portrays the harvesting of salt marsh grasses for feeding livestock in New England, United States.

8. *Waterfowl refuges and migratory stop-overs*

As humans have crowded coastal lands, there has been a sharp reduction in the areas where water-dependent birds can live, and which migrant species can use as stop-overs. These remnant habitats have become ever more critical for conserving the diversity of these water fowl, waders and other aquatic species.

Photo 4.9: Flock of flamingos in a salt marsh. The high production of invertebrates in salt marshes is a magnet for birdlife, contributing to their value for biodiversity conservation.

9. *Interception of land-derived nutrients*

Wetlands intercept certain materials being transported from land to sea. Of the compounds intercepted (not predominantly exported, unlike reduced compounds), one of the most important is nitrate (table 4.7), which powers the production of coastal plants and algae and hence fosters eutrophication. Interception of land-derived nitrate is possible thanks to the high rates of denitrification within salt marshes and mangroves and the burial of nitrogen in their sediments. Evidence of the powerful influence of such interception of land-derived nitrate is the relationship between salt marshes and seagrass meadows: the greater the area of wetland, the greater the production by seagrasses and the smaller the seagrass area lost (figure 4.11.A and B). These linkages occur because seagrasses are highly sensitive to increased nitrogen loads: the presence of a fringe of nitrogen-intercepting wetlands favors the survival of seagrass meadows. Where we see healthy seagrasses, we also often find a fringe of salt marsh interposed between land and sea.

Figure 4.11: Relationship between percent seagrass production (of total production) vs. wetland area of total estuary (A) and percent seagrass area lost vs. wetland area of total estuary (B)

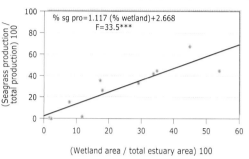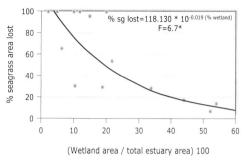

10. *Values for ecotourism and other aesthetic purposes*

Many of us share an appreciation for the aesthetic value of wetlands, as encapsulated in painterly images (figure 4.10). The development of public enjoyment of open space and interest in the fauna of wetlands—particularly birds—has opened up a nascent ecotourism industry involving visits to wetland sites. It is hard to know how to weigh these aspects, but in our urgency to make credible, concrete arguments we would be remiss to ignore the intangible attractiveness of coastal wetlands as additional reasons for their preservation and maintenance.

It would require far more space than we have here to detail the consequences of loss of coastal wetlands and the ecological services listed above. Moreover, there are surely considerable local differences from one part of the world to another. Here we limit our argument to saying, first, that it should be apparent from the preceding list of wetland services that these environments play multifaceted and important functions in the world's coastal regions. They also play fundamental roles in linkages among adjoining coastal ecosystems.

Second, the substantive ecological services provided by coastal wetlands are strongly correlated to wetland area (Turner 1992) or wetland fringe (Gosselink 1984; Brower et al. 1989). As we lose wetland area or fringe, we stand to lose the subsidies provided by these ecosystems.

Third, wetland losses ought to be of concern to people, because, as we argue above, the loss of wetland services matters ecologically and has economic implications. In fact, speculations on ecological valuation (Costanza et al. 1997) have concluded that coastal wetlands are among the most valuable parcels of the world's environments, owing to the many recognized ecological, conservation, water quality, and economic services they perform.

To sum up, the losses of coastal wetlands that are taking place worldwide are quantitatively significant, are apparently increasing and, more importantly, will have ecological and human impacts. We lack sufficient information with which to comprehensively and quantitatively assess the consequences of coastal wetland loss. Obtaining such relationships might be a good way to point the directions for future research in this study area. Efforts to define the functions linking wetland loss and services will require much interdisciplinary collaboration, and will have to cope with the likely spatial heterogeneity of the effects and possibly complex interactions.

We do know enough, however, to conclude that we have lost, globally and locally, a substantial part of the wetlands of the world, that these are key parcels of land- and seascapes, that the services these wetlands can furnish are of consequence ecologically, economically and socially, and that human activities, directly and indirectly, have been instrumental in their decline. It therefore seems imperative to plan concerted action to 1) prevent further losses, 2) preserve and maintain present habitats, and 3) foster efforts to restore lost habitats and create new wetlands.

4.5. THE RESTORATION OF COASTAL WETLANDS

In this essay we have focused on losses and services and said little about the very substantial efforts being made to restore wetland areas. The restoration or construction of coastal wetlands has a lengthy history, and reasonably feasible and economical techniques are available for such measures. Wetlands indeed have good regenerative abilities. One major effort that provides an example of salt marsh restoration is taking place on the Delaware River estuary, using innovative methods which have so far brought successful results (Teal and Weinstein 2002; Teal and Peterson 2005; Teal and Weishar 2005). Although the replanting of mangrove seedlings may fail on occasion, as happened in Samoa, there are many examples of successful mangrove forest restoration (Gilman and Ellison 2007): appropriate contour preparation to allow the recolonization of sediments by mangrove seedlings or the planting of mangrove seedlings has led to the recovery of Florida mangrove stands in the space of a few years.

Much has been done to evaluate whether or not reconstructions lead to the full restoration of services, and the evidence is uneven, though still coming in. But surely, reestablishing lost vegetative stands is a step in the right direction, building on the good start already made. Restoration planning must consider

Photo 4.10: Mangrove forests can be continuous habitats or form a patchy landscape with fringes and lagoons

the past conditions of sites and the causes of their decline, so remedial measures can avoid the conditions that led to the initial losses.

REFERENCES

ADAM, P. "Saltmarshes in a time of change." *Environmental Conservation* 29 (2002): 39-61.

ALBER, M., E. M. SWENSON, S. C. ADAMOWICZ, and I. A. MENDELSSOHN. "Salt marsh dieback: An overview of recent events in the US." *Estuarine, Coastal and Shelf Science* 80 (2008): 1-11.

ALONGI, D. "Resilience of mangrove forests, and effects of tsunamis and global climate change." *Estuarine, Coastal and Shelf Science* (in press).

ALONGI, D. M. "Present state and future of the world's mangrove forests." *Environmental Conservation* 29 (2002): 331-349.

BACKUS, R. H., and D. W. BOURNE, eds. *Georges Bank.* Cambridge, MA: MIT Press, 1987.

BAKER, A. C., P. W. GLYNN, and B. REIGL. "Climate change and coral reef bleaching: An ecological assessment of long-term impacts, recovery trends and future outlook." *Estuarine, Coastal and Shelf Science* 80 (2008): 435-471.

BERTNESS, M. D., C. HOLDREDGE, and A. ALTIERI. "Substrate-type mediates control of salt marsh primary productivity in Cape Cod, MA." *Ecology* (in press).

BLASCO, F., M. AIZPURU, and C. GERS. "Depletion of the mangroves of continental Asia." *Wetlands Ecology and Management* 9 (2001): 245-256.

BLOSSEY, B. http://www.invasiveplants.net/phragmites/morphology.htm. 2002.

BRINKMAN, R. E., S. R. MASSEL, P. V. RIDD, and K. FURUKAWA. "Surface wave attenuation in mangrove forests." *Proceedings of the 13th Australasian Coastal and Ocean Engineering Conference* 2 (1997): 941-949.

BROMBERG, K. D., and M. D. BERTNESS. "Reconstructing New England salt marsh losses using historical maps." *Estuaries* 28 (2005): 823-832.

BROWER, J. A., L. N. MAY JR., A. ROSENTHAL, J. G. GOSSELINK, and R. H. BAUMANN. "Modeling future trends in wetland loss and brown shrimp production in Louisiana using Thematic Mapper imagery." *Remote Sensing of Environment* 28 (1989): 45-59.

CALLAHAN, S. D., and R.W. SCHNEIDER. "Pathogenicity of selected fungi on *Spartina alterniflora* and their possible role in Louisiana's marsh dieback." Abstract. Annual American Phytopathological Society Meeting, July 31–August 4, 2004, Anaheim, CA, 2004.

CHEN, H., B. LI, J. HU, J. CHEN, and J. WU. "Effects of *Spartina alterniflora* invasion on benthic nematode communities in the Yangtze Estuary." *Marine Ecology Progress Series* 336 (2007): 99-110.

CLOERN, J. E. "Does the benthos control phytoplankton biomass in South San Francisco Bay?" *Marine Ecology Progress Series* 9 (1982): 191-202.

COSTANZA R., R. d'ARGE, R. DE GROOT, S. FARBER, M. GRASSO, B. HANNON, K. LIMBURG et al. "The value of the world's ecosystem services and natural capital." *Nature* 387 (1997): 253-60.

CULBERTSON, J. B., I. VALIELA, M. PICKART, E. E. PEACOCK, and C. REDDY. "Long-term consequences of residual petroleum on salt marsh grass in Wild Harbor, MA." *Journal of Applied Ecology* 45 (2008): 1284-1292.

DOODY, J. P. "Coastal squeeze: A historical perspective." *Journal of Coastal Conservation* 10 (2004): 138.

DOW, C. L., and D. R. DEWALLE. "Trends in evaporation and Bowen ratio on urbanizing watersheds in the eastern United States." *Water Resources Research* 36 (2000): 1835-1843.

DOWNS, L. L., R. J. NICHOLLS, S. P. LEATHERMAN, and J. HAUTZENRODER. "Historic evolution of a marsh island: Bloodsworth Island, Maryland." *Journal of Coastal Research* 10 (1994): 1031-1044.

DUKE, N. C., J-O MEYNECKE, S. DITTMANN, A. M. ELLISON, K. ANGER, U. BERGER, S. CANNICCI, et al. "A world without mangroves?" *Science* 317 (2007): 41-42.

EDWARDS, K. R., S. E. TRAVIS, and C. E. PROFFITT. "Genetic effects of a large-scale *Spartina alterniflora* (smooth cordgrass) dieback and recovery in the northern Gulf of Mexico." *Estuaries* 28 (2005): 204-214.

ELLISON, J. C. "Mangrove retreat with rising sea-level, Bermuda." *Estuarine, Coastal and Shelf Science* 37 (1993): 75-87.

FIELD, C. "Impact of expected climate change on mangroves." In Y. Wong and N. F. Tam, eds. *Proceedings of the Asia-Pacific Symposium on Mangrove Ecosystems*, 1995. 75-81, Hydrobiologia, Vol. 295, no. 1-3.

FLORY, J., and M. ALBER. *Dead Marsh Information.* Georgia Coastal Research Council. November 2002.

GEORGIA COASTAL RESEARCH COUNCIL. 2001. http://www..marsci.uga.edu/coastalcouncil/marsh_dieback.htm.

GOODMAN, P. J., E. M. BRAYBROOKS, and J. M. LAMBERT. "Investigations into "die-back" in *Spartina townsendii* Agg.: I. The present status of *Spartina townsendii* in Britain." *Journal of Ecology 47* (1959): 651-677.

GOSSELINK, J. G. *The ecology of delta marshes of coastal Louisiana: A community profile.* FWS/OBS-84/09, Office of Biological Services, U.S. Fish and Wildlife Service, 1984.

GILLMAN, E., H. VAN LAVIEREN, J. ELLISON, V. JUNGBLUT, L. WILSON, F. AREKI, G. BRIGHOUSE, et al. "Pacific Island Mangroves in a Changing Climate and Rising Sea." *UNEP Regional Seas Report and Studies No. 179.* Nairobi, 2006.

GILMAN, E., and J. ELLISON. "Efficacy of alternative low-cost approaches to mangrove restoration, American Samoa." *Estuaries and Coasts* 30 (2007): 641-651.

HARADA, K., and F. IMAMURA. "Effects of coastal forest on tsunami hazard mitigation-A preliminary investigation." *Advances in Natural and Technological Hazards Research* 23 (2005): 279-292.

HARTIG, E. K., V. GORNITZ, A. KOLKER, F. MUSHACKE, and D. FALLON. "Anthropogenic and climate-change impacts on salt marshes of Jamaica Bay, New York City." *Wetlands* 22 (2002): 71-89.

HE, B., T. LAI, H. FAN, W. WANG, and H. ZHENG. "Comparison of flood-tolerance in four mangrove species in diurnal tidal zone in the Beibu Gulf." *Estuarine, Coastal and Shelf Science* 74 (2007): 254-262.

HOLDREDGE, C., M. D. BERTNESS, and A. ALTIERI. "Crab herbivory drives cordgrass die-off in New England salt marshes." *Conservation Biology* (in press).

HONCULADA-PRIMAVERA, J. "Mangroves and brackishwater pond culture in the Philippines." *Hydrobiologia* 295 (1995): 303-309.

HOPKINSON, C. S., JR. "Shallow water benthic and pelagic metabolism: Evidence of heterotrophy in the nearshore Georgia Bight." *Marine Biology* 87 (1985): 19-32.

IPCC (Intergovernmental Panel on Climate Change). *Climate Change 1995: The Science of Climate Change: Contribution of Working Group I to the Second Assessment Report of the Intergovernmental Panel on Climate Change.* J. T. Houghton, L.G. Meira Filho, B. A. Callander, N. Harris, A. Kattenberg, and K. Maskell, eds. Cambridge: Cambridge University Press, 1996.

IPCC (Intergovernmental Panel on Climate Change). *Climate Change 2007: The Physical Science Basis: Contribution of Working Group I to the Fourth Assessment Report of the Intergovernmental Panel on Climate Change.* S. Solomon, D. Qin, M. Manning, Z. Chen, M. Marquis, K. B. Averyt, M. Tignor, and H. L. Miller, eds. Cambridge: Cambridge University Press, 2007.

HULL, K. "Ancient mangroves reveal rapid sea-level rise." *Australasian Science* 26 (2005): 31-32.

HUNTER, K. L., A. DEWAYNE, L. M. BROWN, and K. W. ABLE. "Responses of resident marsh fishes to stages of *Phragmites australis* invasions in three Mid-Atlantic estuaries." *Estuaries and Coasts* 29 (2006): 487-498.

KEARNEY M. S., A. S. ROGERS, J. R. G. TOWNSHEND, E. RIZZO, D. STUTZER, J. C. STEVENSON, and K. SUNDBERG. "Landsat imagery shows decline of coastal marshes in Chesapeake and Delaware Bays." *EOS, Transactions, American Geophysical Union* 83 (2002): 173.

KING, R. S., W. V. DeLuca, D. F. Whigham, and P. P. Marra. "Threshold effects of coastal urbanization on *Phragmites australis* (common reed) abundance and foliar nitrogen in Chesapeake Bay." *Estuaries and Coasts* 30 (2007): 469-481.

Lewis, R. R. "Ecological engineering for successful management and restoration of mangrove forests." *Ecological Engineering* 24 (2005): 403-418.

Ma, Z., X. Gan, C. Choi, K. Jing, S. Tang, B. Li, and J. Chen. "Wintering bird communities in newly-formed wetland in the Yangtze River estuary." *Ecological Research* 22 (2007): 115-124.

Manson, R. A., N. R. Lonegran, G. A. Skilleter, and S. R. Phinn. "An evaluation of the evidence for linkages between mangroves and fisheries: A synthesis of the literature and identification of research directions." *Oceanography and Marine Biology: An Annual Review* 43 (2005): 483-513.

Mazda, Y., E. Wolanski, and P. V. Ridd. *The Role of Physical Processes in Mangrove Environments: Manual for the Preservation and Utilization of Mangrove Ecosystems.* Tokyo: Terrapub, 2007.

McKee, K. L., I. A. Mendelssohn, and M. D. Materne. "Acute salt marsh dieback in the Mississippi River deltaic plain: A drought-induced phenomenon?" *Global Ecology and Biogeography* 13 (2004): 65-73.

Mackenzie, C. L., Jr. "A guide for enhancing estuarine molluscan shellfisheries." *Marine Fisheries Review* 51 (1989): 1-47.

Nicholls, R. J., F. M. J. Hoozemans, and M. Marchand. "Increasing flood risk and wetland losses due to global sea-level rise: Regional and global analyses." *Global Environmental Change* 9 (1999): S69-S87.

Nixon, S. W. *The Ecology of New England High Marshes: A Community Profile.* Fish and Wildlife Service, Office of Biological Services, Vol. FWS/OBS-81/55. U.S. Department of the Interior, Washington, DC, 1982.

Ogburn, M.B., and M. Alber. "An investigation of salt marsh dieback in Georgia using field transplants." *Estuaries* 29 (2006): 54-62.

Packett, C. R., and R. M. Chambers. "Distribution and nutrient status of haplotypes of the marsh grass *Phragmites australis* along the Rappahannock River in Virginia." *Estuaries and Coasts* 29 (2006): 1222-1225.

Peacock, E. "Long-term petroleum hydrocarbon contamination of New England salt marshes: persistence, degradation, and sediment erosion." M.A. thesis, Boston University Marine Program, Boston University, 2007.

Perry, C., and K. G. Taylor, eds. *Environmental Sedimentology.* Oxford: Blackwell Publishing, 2007.

Radeloff V. C., R. B. Hammer, S. I. Stewart, J. S. Fried, S. S. Holcomb, and J. F. McKeefry. "The wildland-urban interface in the United States." *Ecological Applications* 15 (2005): 799-805.

Reed, D. J. "The impact of sea-level rise on coastal salt marshes." *Progress in Physical Geography* 14 (1990): 465-481.

Saltonstall, K. "Cryptic invasion by a non-native genotype of the common reed, *Phragmites australis*, into North America." *Proceedings of the National Academy of Sciences* 99 (2002): 2445-2449.

Saltonstall, K., and J. C. Stevenson. "The effect of nutrients on seedling growth of native and introduced *Phragmites australis*." *Aquatic Botany* 86 (2007): 331-336.

SAENGER, P. *Mangrove Ecology, Silviculture, and Conservation.* Dordrecht: Kluwer Academic Publishers, 2002.

SEMENUIK, V. "Predicting the effect of sea-level rise on mangroves in northwestern Australia." *Journal of Coastal Research* 10 (1994): 1050-1076.

SHUMWAY, S. E., C. DAVIS, R. DOWNEY, R. KARNEY, J. KRAEUTER, J. PARSONS, R. RHEAULT, and G. WIKFORS. "Shellfish aquaculture – in praise of sustainable economies and environments." *World Aquaculture* 34 (2003): 15-18.

SMITH, S. M. *Report on Salt Marsh Dieback on Cape Cod.* National Park Service, Cape Cod National Seashore, Wellfleet, MA, 2006.

SMITH, S. M. "Multi-decadal changes in salt marshes of Cape Cod, Massachusetts: a photographic analysis of vegetation loss, species shifts, and geomorphic change." *Northeastern Naturalist* (in press).

SNEDAKER, S. C. "Mangroves and climate change in the Florida and Caribbean region: Scenarios and hypotheses." *Hydrobiologia* 259 (1995): 43-49.

TANAKA, N., Y. SASAKI, M. I. M. MOWJOOD, K. B. S. N. JINADASA, and S. HOMCHUEN. "Coastal vegetation structures and their function in tsunami protection: Experience of the recent Indian Ocean tsunami." *Landscape and Ecological Engineering* 3 (2007): 33-45.

TEAL, J. M., and S. B. PETERSON "Introduction to the Delaware Bay salt marsh restoration." *Ecological Engineering* 25 (2005): 199-203.

TEAL, J. M., and L. WEISHAR. "Ecological engineering, adaptive management, and restoration management in Delaware Bay salt marsh restoration." *Ecological Engineering* 25 (2005): 304-314.

TEAL, J. M., and M. P. WEINSTEIN. "Ecological engineering, design, and construction considerations for marsh restoration in Delaware Bay, USA." *Ecological Engineering* 18 (2002): 607-618.

TURNER, R. E. "Coastal wetlands and penaeid shrimp habitat." In R.H. Shroud, ed. *Stemming the Tide of Coastal Fish Habitat Loss.* National Coalition for Marine Conservation. Savannah, GA, 1992. 97-104.

TWILLEY, R. R. "Properties of mangrove ecosystems related to the energy signature of coastal environments." In C. A. S. Hall, ed. *Maximum Power: The Ideas and Applications of H. T. Odum.* Boulder, CO: University of Colorado Press, 1995. 43-62.

TWILLEY, R. R. "Coupling of mangroves to the productivity of estuarine and coastal waters." In *Coastal-Offshore Ecosystems Interactions. Lecture Notes on Coastal and Estuarine Studies No. 22.* Berlin: Springer-Verlag, 1998. 155-180.

ULANOWICZ, R. E., and J. H. TUTTLE. "The trophic consequences of oyster stock rehabilitation in Chesapeake Bay." *Estuaries* 15 (1992): 298-306.

VALIELA, I. *Global Coastal Change.* Oxford: Blackwell Publishing, 2006.

VALIELA, I., J. L. BOWEN, and J. K. YORK. "Mangrove forests: One of the world's most threatened major tropical environments." *BioScience* 51 (2001a): 807-815.

VALIELA I., J. L BOWEN, M. L. COLE, K. D. KROEGER, D. LAWRENCE, W. J. PABICH, G. TOMASKY, et al. "Following up on a Margalevian concept: Interactions and exchanges among adjacent parcels of coastal landscapes." *Scientia Marina* 65 (2001b): 215-229.

VAN BREEMEN, N., E. W. BOYER, C. L. GOODALE, N. A. JAWORSKI, K. PAUSTIAN, S. P. SEITZINGER, K. LAJTHA, et al. "Where did all the nitrogen go? Fate of nitrogen inputs to large watersheds in the northeastern U.S.A." *Biogeochemistry* 57-58 (2002): 267-293.

VASQUEZ, E. A., E. P. GLENN, G. R. GUNTENSPERGEN, J. J. BROWN, and S. G. NELSON. "Salt tolerance and osmotic adjustment of *Spartina alterniflora* (Poaceae) and the invasive haplotype of *Phragmites australis* (Poaceae) along a salinity gradient." *American Journal of Botany* 93 (2006): 1784-1790.

VER, L. M. B., F. T. MACKENZIE, and A. LERMAN. "The carbon cycle in the coastal zone: Effects of global perturbations and change in the past three centuries." *Chemical Geology* 159 (1999): 283-304.

WERME, C. E. "Resource Partitioning in a Salt Marsh Fish Community." PhD dissertation, Boston University, 1981.

WILKINSON, C. R. "Global and local threats to coral reef functioning and existence: Review and predictions." *Marine Freshwater Research* 50 (1999): 867-878.

WOLTERS, M., J. P. BAKKER, M. D. BERTNESS, R. L. JEFFERIES, and I. MÖLLER. "Salt marsh erosion and restoration in south-east England: Squeezing the evidence requires realignment." *Journal of Applied Ecology* 42 (2005): 844-851.

WYRTKI, K., and S. NAKAHORO. "Monthly Maps of Sea Level Anomalies in the Pacific 1975-1981. *Hawaii Institute of Geophysics Report* HIG-84-3. Hawaii: Hawaii Institute of Geophysics, 1984.

5. CONFRONTING THE GLOBAL DECLINE OF CORAL REEFS

Terry Hughes
Australian Research Council Center of Excellence for Coral Reef Studies
James Cook University
Townsville, Australia

5.1. INTRODUCTION

HUMAN IMPACTS HAVE RESULTED in dramatic shifts in species composition in many marine and terrestrial ecosystems. These phase shifts are often long-lasting and difficult to reverse. Examples include the replacement of corals by sediment or algal blooms, changes caused by new diseases and invasions by exotic species, and the collapse of coastal and oceanic fisheries. Often these changes occur suddenly and emerge following a natural disturbance that is part of the ecosystem's normal dynamics. Instead of regenerating as they have done for millennia, many coral reefs have lost their capacity to recover from natural perturbations. A new approach to understanding the decline of ecosystems focuses on the concept of "resilience"—the extent to which ecosystems can absorb recurrent natural and human perturbations without switching suddenly or gradually into an alternative (usually degraded) state (Scheffer and Carpenter 2003). Anticipating and preventing unwanted phase shifts on coral reefs requires a better understanding of the processes that support or undermine resilience, and of the social and economic conditions that influence how people use and interact with reefs (Nyström, Folke, and Moberg 2000; Alcala and Russ 2006).

The world's coral reefs support the livelihoods of well over 250 million people, providing food and other resources and supporting a global tourism industry. Coral reefs also have enormous cultural, environmental, and aesthetic value. Yet the world's tropical reefs are in trouble. The Global Coral Reef Monitoring Network has produced summary reports from up to 97 countries in 17 regions, in 1998, 2000, 2002, 2004, and 2008. According to their most recent global assessment, an estimated 34% of the world's coral reefs have already been destroyed or are in imminent danger of collapse, with a further 20% assessed as being under threat of loss within 20-40 years (Wilkinson

◀ **Photo 5.1: Coral formation with individuals of the *Acropora* genus, Thailand.** Coral reefs support amazing diversity, including many species of hard and soft corals.

2008). Even for reefs that are isolated and relatively untouched, global warming and ocean acidification are growing concerns.

The principle human impacts on coral reefs are overfishing, declining water quality (from coastal development and land clearing), and climate change. Importantly, these are not separate issues, because they are highly interactive and they are occurring simultaneously on most reefs around the world. For example, reefs that are overfished and/or polluted often fail to recover after coral bleaching caused by global warming, instead becoming overgrown by blooms of seaweed or other weedy species (photo 5.2). These degraded reefs provide fewer economic options for sustaining coastal communities, especially in developing countries where most tropical reefs occur. Two case studies examined below, the Caribbean and the Great Barrier Reef, illustrate some of these issues from contrasting biogeographic and socioeconomic settings.

One way to view human impacts on coral reefs is to consider how overfishing and pollution affect the structure of foodwebs. The removal of species near the

Photo 5.2: Algal blooms. Promoted by added nutrients and overfishing, algal blooms are a major threat to coral reefs. Fleshy seaweed can outcompete corals, preventing recruitment by juveniles and overgrowing and shading adults.

top of a foodweb by fishing can lead to an increase in abundance of their prey (called a top-down effect). Many reefs worldwide have been severely over-fished. Megafauna such as sharks and turtles are increasingly rare worldwide, and in many places fisheries have moved lower down the foodweb, targeting increasing numbers of herbivores such as parrotfish. Similarly, the addition of nutrients can stimulate growth of species at the bottom of the foodweb (primary producers such as phytoplankton and fleshy seaweed). This bottom-up effect can propagate upwards in a foodweb by providing more food for filter-feeders, herbivores and, in turn, for their predators. Top-down and bottom-up distortions of foodwebs typically happen simultaneously.

Natural disturbances (e.g., hurricanes or cyclones, floods, tsunamis, unusually low tides) play a role that is similar to fires in terrestrial systems, continually opening up space and maintaining the local diversity of reefs by preventing overcrowding. Corals and other reef organisms have evolved complex regenerative mechanisms which allow them to recover from a wide variety of natural sources of mortality such as storms, predation, and routine levels of disease. Therefore, human impacts are superimposed on the natural turnover and dynamics of coral reefs, causing elevated rates of mortality and—just as importantly—reduced rates of regeneration (e.g., due to sublethal impacts on reproduction, larval settlement, and survival of new recruits).

5.2. SHIFTING BASELINES, HISTORY, AND THE FOSSIL RECORD

In recent years, reef scientists have been taking a longer view of reef dynamics. Historical trajectories of reef degradation help to reveal the gradual erosion of ecological resilience that can lead to sudden ecosystem collapse, as well as providing insights into appropriate management interventions. Ignoring or denying trajectories of change leads to complacency and inaccurate perceptions that reefs are stable or "pristine". A longer timeframe focuses attention on the cumulative and interactive effects of sequences of events, rather than concentrating solely on the most recent insult that can lead finally to ecosystem collapse (Jackson et al. 2001).

Most coral reefs today are highly altered ecosystems. In many countries, the current system of governance and management of coral reefs were instigated long after reefs became significantly degraded, with the goal of sustaining whatever remained. Typically, management targets slip lower and lower over time as reefs continue to decline and the memory of their former status fades, a scenario known as "the shifting baseline" (Pauly 1995). Today, for example,

143

younger Caribbean researchers and managers may never have seen a healthy thicket of Caribbean *Acropora* coral, a manatee, or a large shark. Shifting baselines such as these pervade coral reef science and management.

Corals and other calcifying organisms (e.g., coralline algae, mollusks, bryozoans) have an excellent fossil record which provides invaluable insights into the species composition and dynamics of reefs in the past. The same species alive today have dominated coral reefs for the past half million years, with one obvious exception, *Homo sapiens*. The fossil record, therefore, provides a unique baseline that long predates the influence of humans (Pandolfi et al. 2003). Historical analysis shows that reef megafauna (turtles, dugongs, sharks) declined before small animals and corals, and that Caribbean reefs declined earlier and to a much greater extent than reefs in the Red Sea and Pacific. The trajectories of decline and sequence of degradation were very similar worldwide, and nowhere can be considered today to be "pristine". Many reefs were significantly degraded long before more recent outbreaks of coral disease and bleaching associated with contemporary global warming.

Recent glacial-interglacial cycles caused the sea to repeatedly flood and drain from continental shelves and oceanic islands. For example, the Great Barrier Reef in Queensland, Australia was high and dry at the end of the last ice age, when sea level was >100 meters lower than today. Heron Island, which today lies 70 km offshore from mainland Australia, was then a hill more than 100 km inland. The coastline was much more exposed to oceanic conditions than today, and the area of shallow water habitat was a small fraction of its current extent. Sea level rose rapidly from 14,000 years before the present, stabilizing at close to its current level 6,000 years ago. In the broadest parts of Queensland's continental shelf, the water raced sideways at an average rate of more than 50 cm per week for several thousand years. Inshore habitats dominated by mangroves, seagrass, and oyster beds increased dramatically, and corals once more re-invaded the newly submerged shelf. Many marine species exhibit a genetic legacy of these substantial population fluctuations and range shifts caused by past climate change.

The anticipated rise in sea level over the next 50 years due to contemporary global warming is relatively tiny compared to the recent historical rises at the end of the last ice age, because today the world's oceans are already at a high sea-level stand. Sea level rise and coastal flooding in the coming decades will be a much more serious issue for people in low-lying countries than it will be for coral reefs. Higher temperature due to global warming is a much more serious issue than sea-level rise for corals, because many species are already close to their maximal thermal limits. The expected increases in temperature and atmospheric carbon dioxide over the next 50 years will substantially exceed the conditions under which coral reefs have flourished over the past half million years. There is one other major difference between the future and past responses to climate change by coral reefs: this time reefs will also have to cope with the activities of more than six billion people. Over the past few hundred years, accelerating human impacts have undermined the resilience of coral reefs, increasing their vulnerability to future climate change.

5.3. BIOGEOGRAPHY HOTSPOTS AND CONSERVATION PRIORITIES

Biodiversity hotspots, regions with exceptionally high species richness, are often identified as prime targets for the protection of marine ecosystems. However, there are several new lines of evidence to suggest that "cool spots", areas of low species richness, are even more vulnerable. The major coral reef biodiversity hotspot is located in the central Indo-Pacific, a large triangular region centered on Indonesia, Malaysia, Papua New Guinea, and the Philip-

Photo 5.3: Coral reef covered with soft corals (*Sarcophyton trochelioporum*), Philippines, Pacific Ocean

pines (lying between 10°S-10°N and 100°-140°E). In general, the diversity of corals and other reef-associated species declines latitudinally away from the central Indo-Pacific hotspot (which straddles the equator), as well as longitudinally to the east across the Pacific and westwards across the Indian. Two secondary coral reef hotspots occur in the Red Sea and, to a lesser extent, in the Caribbean. The similarity in regional-scale biodiversity patterns among major groups such as corals, reef fishes, mollusks, and crustaceans points to a shared history and set of mechanisms that exert a broad influence on many taxonomic groups (Bellwood and Hughes 2001).

Widespread concerns over the loss of biodiversity and species extinctions have led many conservation groups and governments to focus on the preservation of hotspots as a priority. Protecting biodiversity hotspots may be the most cost-effective way to protect large numbers of species. In terrestrial systems, biodiversity hotspots generally contain large numbers of species with small geographic ranges (endemics) that are potentially vulnerable to global extinction, especially if they are also numerically rare and specialized. For corals and reef fishes, however, high diversity in the central Indo-Pacific hotspot arises primarily from the overlap of pandemic species, whose ranges stretch from the hotspot westwards across the Indian Ocean to East Africa and/or eastwards to the Central Pacific. Only 1% of 602 Indo-Pacific corals are endemic to the central Indo-Pacific hotspot. Among reef fishes, only 3% have geographic ranges that lie entirely within the hotspot boundaries. For these two crucial groups, corals and reef fishes, the proportion of endemics is highest at depauperate, peripheral regions such as Hawaii, the Eastern Pacific, and at high latitude sub-tropical reefs (Hughes, Bellwood, and Connolly 2002).

5.4. FUNCTIONAL GROUPS, REDUNDANCY, AND BIOGEOGRAPHY

A functional group is defined as a group of species that share a common ecological function, regardless of their taxonomic affinities. An example is reef herbivores, a diverse assemblage that includes many species of fish, echinoids, and other taxa. The depletion or loss of one species in a functional group can potentially be compensated for by other species that share a similar ecological role. Low-diversity coral reefs in the Caribbean and the Eastern Pacific, and at many high-latitude locations in the Indo-Pacific, have low disease, because functional groups there may be absent or represented by just a single species. For example, in the Caribbean there are no weedy bushy corals with high rates of larval recruitment and growth. This functional group of corals is diverse and abundant throughout most of the Pacific and Indian Oceans and the Red Sea (photo 5.4). Caribbean reefs have only a small fraction, about 15%, of the total number of coral species found throughout most of the tropical Indo-Pacific oceans. The most striking taxonomic difference is the generic and species richness of the family Acroporidae. The four Indo-Pacific genera in this family, *Acropora, Anacropora, Astreopora*, and *Montipora*, are represented by over 120 species on the Great Barrier Reef. In marked contrast, only *Acropora*, represented by just two species (*A. palmata, A. cervicornis*, and a hybrid between them) are present today in the

Photo 5.4: A healthy coral reef at Lizard Islands on the northern Great Barrier Reef. Almost all of the corals shown are fast-growing staghorn, bushy, and tabular species of *Acropora*, the dominant genus of corals throughout most of the Indo-Pacific.

Caribbean (photo 5.5). These two species are now increasingly uncommon, due to their failure to recover from mass mortalities caused by hurricanes, algal blooms, sedimentation and runoff, disease, and climate change (Gardener et al. 2003). Loss of species from low-diversity locations affects a disproportionately large proportion of an already depauperate fauna. The widespread decline of *Acropora palmata* and *A. cervicornis*, the only tall three-dimensional corals in the Caribbean, provides a graphic example of the vulnerability of depauperate regions that have little or no disease.

An important issue is whether high species richness confers greater resilience to marine ecosystems. Comparisons of species-rich and naturally depauperate marine systems indicate that higher biodiversity can, in some circumstances, afford a degree of ecological insurance against ecological uncertainty. However, if all species within a functional group respond similarly to pressures such as overfishing or pollution, then higher biodiversity will not afford additional protection. Low-diversity coral reefs of the Caribbean undoubtedly have lower disease than most reefs in the Indo-Pacific, but nevertheless even the most diverse reefs in the world are increasingly threatened by severe overfishing, pollution, and climate change.

Photo 5.5: A Caribbean reef in the 1970s. The image shows the dominance of the robust elkhorn coral, *Acropora palmata*, and the more slender staghorn coral, *Acropora cervicornis*. These two species are increasingly rare due to their vulnerability to coastal runoff, hurricanes, disease, and algal blooms.

5.4.1. Overfishing: impacts on foodwebs and the functioning of ecosystems

Overfishing is a major environmental and economic problem facing virtually all marine ecosystems, including most coral reefs. Typically, overexploitation of a mixed reef fishery first depletes stocks of megafauna and large predators (e.g., turtles, dugongs, sharks, groupers), and subsequently smaller herbivorous and planktivorous fishes become a more prevalent component of the overall catch. For example, in most parts of the Caribbean, parrotfish are a major component of reef fisheries, especially where their predators have long been depleted. Comparisons of lightly and heavily fished coral reefs (e.g., inside and outside of no-take areas) provide compelling evidence for top-down alterations to foodwebs (also called trophic cascades) following the depletion of predators. In the Caribbean and the eastern Pacific, the depletion of fish predators and competitors of echinoids is likely to have played a key role in generating unsustainably high densities of sea urchins. In 1983-4, the abundant Caribbean sea urchin *Diadema antillarum* suffered 99% mortality from disease, which in turn led to dramatic algal blooms that have persisted for the past 25 years. Similarly, the widespread declines of herbivorous and predatory turtles have led to increases in the biomass of seagrasses and sponges (Jackson et al. 2001).

Until recently, fishing on most coral reefs has been largely artisanal, providing a much-needed and cheap source of protein. Even in locations with relatively small human populations, traditional fishing has reduced the abundance of targeted species and changed ecosystem function. For example, the dugong and many species of turtles are ecologically extinct throughout most of their former geographic ranges and are locally abundant only in remote pockets. Similarly, the Indo-Pacific humphead parrotfish, *Bolbometopon muricatum*, has been overfished through most of its geographic range. *Bolbometopon* grows to more than a meter in length, with each adult fish consuming five tonnes of coral per annum (Bellwood, Hoey, and Choat 2003). Its depletion has removed the major external bioeroder from many Indo-Pacific reefs, with poorly understood long-term consequences.

In recent decades, there has been a dramatic increase in fishing effort on coral reefs, and the export of both live and dead coral reef fishes is expanding rapidly. The unprecedented demand for live reef fishes in Southeast Asia is exerting additional fishing pressure on reefs throughout vast areas of the Indo-Pacific. With retail prices of up to US$250 per kg, exploitation of remote reef systems has become financially viable for the first time, overcoming previous cost-barriers. Herbivorous fishes are an increasingly significant component of the live fish

Photo 5.6: The humphead parrotfish (*Bolbometopon muricatum*) has been severely depleted by spear-fishing

trade, ranking currently as the second largest group targeted for exploitation (based on biomass). These new markets for reef fishes have greatly augmented both the intensity and scale of exploitation, and are set to increase as fish stocks elsewhere continue to decline. The depletion of herbivorous fishes combined with runoff of nutrients and increasingly frequent bleaching events is an ominous combination that has led to corals being replaced by blooms of seaweed on numerous reefs around the world (e.g., Hughes 1994; Mumby et al. 2006).

5.4.2. No-take areas

No-take areas, where fishing is prohibited, are important tools for managing foodwebs, ecosystem function, and the resilience of reefs. Traditionally, proponents of no-take areas have focused on their utility for managing targeted fisheries, rather than their potential to regulate the ecosystem functions of harvested stocks, their prey, and the resilience of reef ecosystems. More recently, there has been a growing awareness of the role of no-take areas in maintaining the ecosystem functions provided by reef fishes. In particular, herbivorous fishes play several key roles in the dynamics of tropical reefs: they graze fleshy seaweeds that compete with juvenile and adult corals for space; they erode dead coral skeletons and generate reef sediments; and they support subsistence fisheries on many coral reefs around the world (photo 5.7).

Because most no-take areas on coral reefs were established very recently, only a few studies have been conducted for long enough to demonstrate their long-term effects. The best available time series on the build-up of fish in coral reef no-take areas comes from long-term studies of no-take reserves in the Philippines, where the biomass of large predatory fish has increased at an average annual rate of 12%, to more than six times the biomass of adjacent non-reserves (Russ, Stockwell, and Alcala 2005). Importantly, the build-up of fish stocks showed no sign of leveling off after 19 years of protection. It is sobering to consider that in the timeframe required for comprehensive regeneration of fish stocks in coral reef no-take areas (>20 years), the human population size of developing countries is likely to double. In the Bahamas, scientists have focused on the number and size of grazing parrotfish and their predators and on the abundance of seaweed, both inside and outside a no-take area which was censused after 20 years of protection (Mumby et al. 2006). The biomass of predatory fishes (groupers, barracuda, moray eels, and large snappers) inside the no-take area was double that of adjacent reefs. The biomass of parrotfishes within the no-take area was also significantly higher than in adjacent areas

Photo 5.7: An endangered Caribbean parrotfish, *Scarus gaucamaia*, grazing on small tufts of macroalgae

that support a mixed-species reef fishery. The estimated grazing intensity of parrotfishes was six times higher inside the no-take area, and the cover of seaweed was five times lower compared to adjoining reefs (figure 5.1). This study demonstrates that no-take areas can regulate herbivory; a key ecosystem process for maintaining reef resilience.

Most no-take areas are very small, typically a few hectares. Even the largest ones, such as the Great Barrier Reef Marine Park (which is 33% no-take), are too small to be completely self-sustaining or to fully protect mobile species such as sharks and turtles that are targeted outside the no-take area. Similarly, the flow of larvae of most species across the boundary of no-take areas is extensive and multi-directional, and in many cases the replenishment of local populations within protected areas (including fishes, corals, algae, and pathogens) relies on an *influx* of propagules from outside habitats. Clearly, the success or failure of any no-take area will depend on outside areas that are part of the same highly connected reef system. While no-take areas are an important element in the global response to the coral reef crisis, they are not a panacea, and coordinated management of both no-take and harvested areas is crucial for their long-term sustainability (Hughes et al. 2003; Sale et al. 2005).

Figure 5.1: The effect of protection of herbivorous fishes afforded by no-take areas. The blue bars show the biomass of parrotfish, their grazing intensity, and the abundance of fleshy seaweed inside a no-take area in the Bahamas. The brown bars show lower fish biomass, less grazing, and more seaweed outside the no-take area

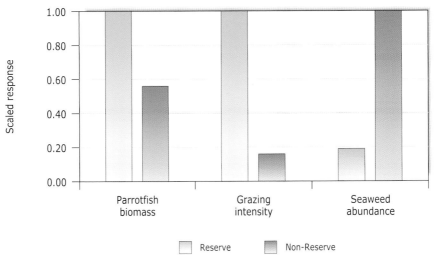

Source: Redrawn from Mumby et al. 2006.

5.5. WATER QUALITY

Runoff from land causes elevated nutrient loads and increased turbidity from suspended sediments. Excessive levels of sedimentation are caused by activities such as soil erosion from agriculture, dredging, coral mining, coastal development, and drilling for oil and gas. The most widespread of these is soil erosion, due to widespread changes in land use practices, increasing the sediment and nutrient levels in rivers that flow onto coastal reefs. Throughout the tropics, there has been widespread deforestation and land clearing for agriculture, aquaculture, and urbanization. Increased turbidity influences the physiology, growth, and survival of corals in several ways. Firstly, corals need to expend energy cleaning themselves of sediment to prevent smothering. Secondly, the amount of light reaching a coral colony is reduced by increased turbidity, slowing their growth. High rates of sedimentation are especially damaging to juvenile corals, which are easily smothered by silt, affecting the ability of reefs to regenerate after disturbances such as cyclones or coral bleaching.

Inputs from sewage and runoff of fertilizers can potentially alter foodwebs (bottom-up effects) and damage coral reefs. The iconic example of sewage effects on a coral reef comes from Kaneohe Bay, Hawaii (Maragos, Evans, and Holtus 1985). The bay is very shallow, connected to the ocean by a narrow opening (i.e., it has a very low flushing rate compared to most coral reefs), and the land area surrounding it is densely populated. Kaneohe Bay has a long history of other impacts such as dredging and overfishing and has a high proportion of pest species introduced by shipping. Sewage was discharged into Kaneohe Bay in the 1960s and 1970s from three outfalls at a rate of up to 20,000 m^3 per day. Several streams also enter the bay, carrying urban and suburban runoff. These conditions increased nutrients and sediment loads, leading to blooms of phytoplankton. Coral patch reefs were colonized by benthic macroalgae and suspension feeders (bivalves and sponges), while coral cover declined sharply. These effects exhibited a gradient away from the sewage outfalls. However, when the nutrient input was reduced, water clarity improved, the filter feeders and algae declined, and the corals slowly increased.

Population explosions of the coral-feeding crown-of-thorns starfish, *Acanthaster planci*, may also be related to widespread nutrient enrichment of coastal waters. These outbreaks were first observed in the late 1950s and 1960s, when many coral reefs in Australia, Guam, Japan, the Red Sea, and elsewhere were badly damaged by enormous densities of starfish. Since then, repeated outbreaks have occurred throughout most of the starfish's geographic range, and they have become a chronic issue on many reefs. Out-

Photo 5.8: The crown-of-thorns starfish (*Acanthaster planci*), a major predator of corals

breaks are initiated by heavy recruitment of juvenile starfish, leading to two theories that propose a link to human activities. One suggests that a top-down alteration of foodwebs has released *Acanthaster* from predation. This seems unlikely since there are very few fisheries for the predators of juvenile or adult starfish. The other theory hypothesizes that added nutrients have led to more phytoplankton food for starfish larvae. This bottom-up effect may have significantly reduced the development time of juvenile starfish, allowing many more of them to survive to settlement, potentially resulting in destructive outbreaks.

5.6. CLIMATE CHANGE

Climate change is not some distant future threat to reefs that may or may not come to pass. Global warming has already caused one or more bouts of coral bleaching on many reefs—roughly half of the world's total—in the past 25 years or so. Some of these reefs appear to be recovering well, but many are not. The projected increases in water temperature, changes in the frequency and intensity of severe storms, and the rising acidity of the oceans all pose profound environmental and socioeconomic challenges, particularly for those reefs that are already stressed due to more local pressures of overfishing and pollution (Hughes et al. 2003)

Coral bleaching occurs when corals become physiologically stressed and lose most of the symbiotic algae (zooxanthellae) that give them most of their color (photo 5.9). Small-scale bleaching has been widely described in older coral reef scientific literature following hot or cold weather and floods. However, regional-scale bleaching is a new phenomenon driven by global warming. In 1998, elevated sea surface temperatures associated with an extreme El Niño event resulted in the largest and most destructive bleaching event yet documented, causing widespread damage that extended from the western Pacific across the Indian Ocean to Africa and severely degrading an estimated 16% of the world's coral reefs (Wilkinson 2000).

Like most forms of disturbance, bleaching affects some species of corals more than others (figure 5.2.A). For example, some coral genera, such as slow-growing, massive or encrusting *Porites* and *Leptastrea*, bleach less readily than faster-growing, branching and tabular *Acropora* (Loya et al. 2001; Marshall and Baird

Photo 5.9: Coral bleaching on the reef slope of Raiatea, French Polynesia. Note that bleaching is selective, with some corals affected more than others (see figure 5.2.A.). Selectivity is important, because it is already altering the species composition of coral assemblages, in favor of species that are relatively resistant to bleaching. Susceptible species are likely to become increasingly rare in the future as further bleaching events occur.

Figure 5.2: Coral bleaching by latitude and temperature. A: Different species of corals (here labeled a-k) show varying susceptibilities to bleaching. 100% represents bleaching by every coral in populations at Raiatea, French Polynesia, during May 2002. **B:** Latitudinal extents of all Indo-pacific reef corals, measured from the northern to the southernmost point in their range. Most species have a latitudinal span of 50-70 degrees, straddling the equator. **C:** Geographic range boundaries of 24 pandemic species of Indo-Pacific corals that are found in the Persian Gulf and at Lord Howe Island off Australia, where average maximum summer temperatures differ by $12^{0}C$. The coloring shows temperatures in the Southern Hemisphere summer of 1997/1998, when unprecedented mass bleaching occurred.

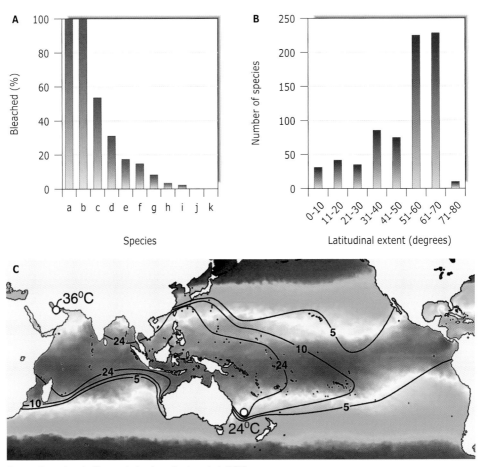

Source: Reproduced with permission from Hughes et al. 2003.

2000). Similarly, recolonization after disturbances such as cyclones or bleaching events varies greatly among coral species, depending on their life histories and the scale of stock-recruitment relationships (how far larvae travel from their source). Therefore, over coming decades some susceptible species may decline or disappear, while others may increase. The long-term impact of rapid temperature rises will depend critically on the ability of corals to acclimatize and/or adapt, and on their capacity to migrate. The fossil record shows dramatic expansions and contractions in the geographic ranges of corals during past periods of warming and cooling, in the Pleistocene and Holocene. Along the coast of western Australia, for example, the geographic boundaries of staghorn corals extended up to 500 km further south (to 33°S) of their current range (27°S). In the past, some species migrated faster than others, producing rapid shifts in species composition, especially near faunal boundaries. This historical evidence suggests that contemporary climate change will also influence the geographic boundaries of species, via changes in their physiology, altered hydrodynamics and dispersal of larvae, and in response to a new mix of species interactions.

Most corals bleach when the sea water temperature exceeds the average summer level of a particular location by about 2°C for more than a few weeks. Importantly, average temperatures often differ by 10°C or more within the geographic range of most coral species, which typically straddle the equator and extend to cooler sub-tropical areas (figure 5.2. B and C). A higher bleaching threshold in warmer locations implies that there is strong selection for corals and their zooxanthellae to evolve thresholds that are near the expected upper temperature at that location. How long this adaptation takes to evolve is unknown, and so a major issue is whether coral and zooxanthellae species can adapt quickly to the rapid climate changes that are now underway.

Corals and their algal symbionts have high levels of genetic diversity, which could promote rapid evolution. Although it is clear that mortality rates from bleaching events are often very high, and the fecundity of surviving corals is often reduced, very little is known about how much selection this exerts or about the heritability of physiological traits. Aquarium studies of the upper thermal tolerances of corals have shown they have some capacity for phenotypic change, or acclimation. Past experience of thermal stress and bleaching can also substantially reduce the susceptibility of corals to subsequent bleaching episodes. Corals on geographically isolated, oceanic reefs are likely to be extremely vulnerable to global warming, even where local threats are minimal, because of their small population size, increased inbreeding, and the near absence of long-distance dispersal by larvae to the sites they occupy.

5.7. TWO CASE STUDIES

Two large-scale cases studies from the Caribbean and the Great Barrier Reef further illustrate the impact of human activities on the condition and dynamics of coral reefs, and the challenges for managing overfishing, pollution, and climate change in different social and economic settings.

5.7.1. The Caribbean

A recent analysis of coral abundance in the Caribbean, based on 65 studies at 263 sites, shows that average cover has declined from 54% in 1977 to just 9% in 2001 (Gardener et al. 2003). This recent collapse was preceded by dwindling stocks of fishes and increased nutrient and sediment runoff from land over the past century and longer. The depletion of fishes led to population explosions of the sea urchin *Diadema antillarum*. In the 1960s and 1970s, the recorded densities of *Diadema* on overfished reefs throughout the Caribbean were extraordinarily high, commonly averaging >20 individuals per m^2 in shallow waters (photo 5.10). On many reefs, this one species had replaced a suite of herbivorous fishes as the main grazer of algae. Consequently, it was the last abundant member of a crucial function group that controlled the abundance of seaweed. At high densities, *Diadema* were small and food-limited, and their grazing activities bulldozed coral recruits and removed more carbonate from live and dead corals than the reef could generate by calcification. The crowded condition of *Diadema* populations may have contributed to their eventual

Photo 5.10: The sea urchin *Diadema antillarum*. The most important herbivore and bioeroder of Caribbean reefs prior to its mass mortality from disease in 1983-4. The disease epidemic prompted blooms of fleshy seaweed, especially on reefs where fish herbivores such as parrotfish were over-exploited. The seaweed prevented recruitment by juvenile corals and slowly smothered and replaced adults. More than 30 years later, only a limited recovery of *Diadema* has occurred, and many reefs remain choked with seaweed.

demise in 1983-4, when a disease outbreak spread throughout the Caribbean, reducing their numbers by 99%.

The trajectory of coral cover over the past 30 years has varied from place to place around the Caribbean, depending on which locations were affected by hurricanes, bleaching events, and disease outbreaks in different years. The fact there has been so much debate about what killed the corals reflects these different sequences of events. In Jamaica, for example, the initial loss of coral cover occurred in 1980 due to Hurricane Allen, which destroyed most of the dense growths of staghorn and elkhorn corals, *Acropora cervicornis* and *A. palmate.* Other locations lost most of their *Acropora* from other hurricanes, runoff of sediments or, more recently, through disease or bleaching events. The debate on mortality, however, misses the crucial point that Caribbean reefs have lost their capacity to regenerate following the recurrent hurricanes these species have experienced for hundreds of thousands of years. The die-off of *Diadema* in Jamaica precipitated blooms of macroalgae that have prevented recovery of corals by inhibiting larval settlement and by smothering juveniles. All species of corals in Jamaica have declined in abundance over the past 30 years, through a combination of elevated mortality, declining brood stocks, and recruitment failure (photo 5.11).

In the past few years, *Diadema* has shown a modest recovery at some locations in the Caribbean. However, it remains an order of magnitude less abundant than

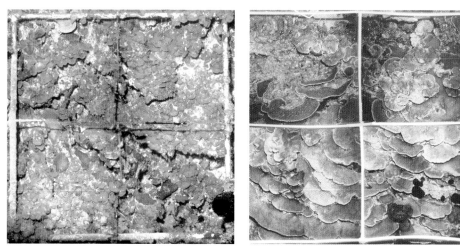

Photo 5.11: Phase shift from a healthy coral assemblage to a persistent algal bloom. This shift is illustrated by a before and after picture of the same 2x2 m quadrant located at a depth of 35 m off Jamaica. The left image records abundant corals in 1981, while the right image shows the same spot twelve years later, in 1993, by which time virtually all of the original corals were smothered by fleshy seaweed and almost no new coral recruits survived.

before the die-off in 1983-4 and is restricted to the shallow end of its former depth range. In 2006, the U.S. Fish and Wildlife Service added the two Caribbean species of *Acropora* to the List of Endangered and Threatened Wildlife. The continued slow recovery of *Diadema* may help to control algal blooms, but it is uncertain whether it will return to dangerously high densities or extend to its former depth range. Chronic overfishing continues throughout most of the Caribbean, and fish stocks remain severely depleted in most regions.

5.7.2. The Great Barrier Reef

Australia's Great Barrier Reef system is in relatively good condition, due in part to its large size, relative isolation, and a long-term investment by governments in reef science and management. Unusually among coral reef nations, Australia has a low population density and is relatively very wealthy. However, the Great Barrier Reef is showing symptoms of change and increased vulnerability that warrant concern. Fisheries that flourished following European colonization (e.g., sea cucumbers, pearl shell, *Trochus* snails, dugongs, whales,

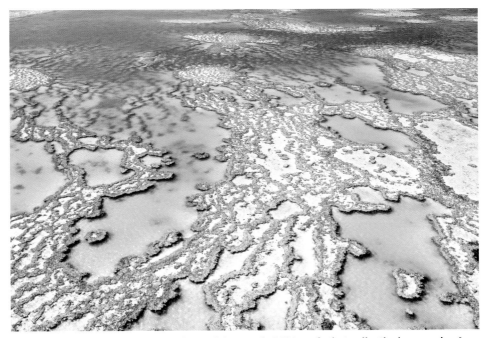

Photo 5.12: An aerial photograph of one of the nearly 3000 reefs that collectively comprise Australia's Great Barrier Reef, the world's largest coral reef system. The Great Barrier Reef has the world's biggest network of no-take areas (where fishing is prohibited) and supports a major international tourism industry.

and turtles) have collapsed or are no longer commercially viable. Runoff of sediment and nutrients from land has increased greatly since the mid-1800s, affecting nearshore reefs and seagrass beds. In the past 40 years, large-scale outbreaks of crown-of-thorns starfish, *Acanthaster planci*, have occurred three times, reducing coral cover on roughly 200 reefs (out of the total number of 2,900 comprising the Great Barrier Reef system). Major bleaching events from climate change struck the Great Barrier Reef in 1998 (during the same El Niño event that damaged reefs elsewhere in the western Pacific and Indian Ocean) and again in 2002, damaging close to 600 individual reefs. Coral cover remains low on reefs affected by runoff, crown-of-thorn starfish, and coral bleaching. Rapid growth in recreational and commercial fishing has reduced the biomass of targeted fish species by more than 80% in heavily fished inshore areas, compared to adjacent no-take reserves (Williamson, Russ, and Ayling 2004). Herbivorous fishes remain abundant and are protected by regulations on fishing gear.

From July 1, 2004, the proportion of the Great Barrier Reef Marine Park closed to fishing (i.e., no-take fishing reserves) was increased from 5% to 33%, encompassing at least 20% of all major habitat types (Fernandes et al. 2005). Simultaneously, a new ten-year program, the Reef Water Quality Protection Plan, was formulated in an attempt to curb future nutrient and sediment runoff. These management changes exemplify a new ecosystem-based approach that arose from a shift in perceptions about the increasing risks to the "once pristine" Great Barrier Reef. The changes in zoning were undertaken to build ecological resilience and to cope proactively with the risk associated with human population growth, rising fishing pressure, future bleaching events, and other uncertainties. Australia belatedly ratified the Kyoto Protocol in 2008, following a change of national government.

5.8. FUTURE PROSPECTS

Building the resilience of coral reefs to avoid phase shifts provides a new framework for preserving and managing these important ecosystems. There is growing awareness among reef managers of the functional role of fishes, the effects of overfishing on the dynamics of foodwebs, and the bottom-up influence of pollution. In particular, preserving stocks of fishes and reducing runoff of nutrients and sediment are increasingly seen as ways to maximize the resilience of coral reefs. Local controls on fishing and water quality can also provide some insurance against larger-scale ecological surprises (such as coral bleaching) that are impractical to manage directly in the short term. Preventing coral bleaching is not a tractable management goal at a local level (because it will require global reductions of greenhouse gases). On the other hand, building and supporting resilience in anticipation of bleaching and other recurrent disturbances can be achieved locally by changing destructive human activities (e.g., overfishing and pollution). However, local action will not be enough on its own to prevent the ongoing destruction of reefs due to rapid climate change. An urgent reduction in the world's greenhouse gas emissions is essential for reducing the severe impact of thermal stress and ocean acidification on coral reefs.

Predicting and preventing unwanted phase shifts (or, conversely, promoting desirable ones) is a major challenge for future research, which will require a much better understanding of the complex processes that support or erode resilience. The focus needs to shift from the conventional monitoring and mapping of bio-diversity and species abundances towards active management of key functional groups that support important processes and sustain ecosystem services. Moni-toring programs urgently need to be improved, to gain a clearer understanding of critical thresholds and feedbacks, and of the capacity of coral reefs to contin-ue to provide ecological services such as fisheries and tourism. Developing and testing new metrics for the stewardship of coral reef resilience (e.g., stock sizes of herbivorous fishes, rates of coral recruitment and regeneration, disease) is critical for coping with uncertainty and future ecological surprises.

Restoring coral reef ecosystems after they have undergone a phase shift is much more difficult than maintaining them in good condition, as shown above by the two case studies. The timeframe for recouping depleted fish stocks and for improving regional water quality is typically decades not months, and indeed may not always be socially, economically or biologically feasible. Some severe-ly degraded coral reefs have changed to the extent that they are unlikely to recover and regain their original configuration, because a new set of feedbacks have locked them into a new state. For example, regeneration of coral reefs can be inhibited by a surfeit of coral predators, by recruitment failure following the loss of brood stocks, by blooms of resilient algae that resist herbivory and smother juvenile corals, or by persistent layers of sediment. Similarly, because of their slow growth, a complete reversal of the ecological extinction of megafauna on most coral reefs would take centuries, even if hunting pressure disappeared and all lost habitat was restored. Clearly, it is easier to sustain a resilient ecosystem than to repair it after a phase shift has occurred.

Recovery of degraded coral reefs that are chronically impacted by people will not be possible unless the major ongoing drivers (e.g., greenhouse gas emis-sions, runoff of sediment, excess nutrients, and fishing pressure) are first

Photo 5.13: Coral community in the Philippines. Reefs provide critical ecosystem goods and services to local people, principally through fisheries and tourism. As a consequence, sustaining coral reefs is not just a goal for conserving biodiversity. It is also a social and economic imperative.

reduced. No-take areas can play an important role in rebuilding fish stocks and the structure of foodwebs. However, there is also an urgent need to improve management measures for the vast majority of reefs that are heavily impacted by people, because no-take areas are tightly linked to the broader seascape. Establishing appropriate multi-scale systems of governance that are strongly supported by local, national, and international communities is undoubtedly the major challenge for the future of coral reefs.

REFERENCES

ALCALA, A. C., and G. R. RUSS. "No-take marine reserves and reef fisheries management in the Philippines: a new people power revolution." *Ambio* 35 (2006): 245-254.

BELLWOOD D. R., T. P. HUGHES, C. FOLKE, and M. NYSTRÖM. "Confronting the coral reef crisis." *Nature* 429 (2004): 827-33

BELLWOOD, D. R., A. S. HOEY, and J. H. CHOAT. "Limited functional redundancy in high diversity systems: resilience and ecosystem function on coral reefs." *Ecology Letters* 6 (2003): 281-285.

FERNANDES, L., J. DAY, A. LEWIS, S. SLEGERS, B. KERRIGAN, D. BREEN, D. CAMERON, et al. "Establishing representative no-take areas in the Great Barrier Reef: large-scale implementation of theory on Marine Protected Areas." *Conservation Biology* 19 (2005): 1733-1744.

GARDENER, T. A., I. COTE, J. A. GILL, A. GRANT, and A. R. WATKINSON. "Long-term region-wide declines in Caribbean corals." *Science* 301 (2003): 958-960.

HUGHES, T. P. "Catastrophes, phase shifts, and large-scale degradation of a Caribbean reef." *Science* 265 (1994): 1547-1551.

HUGHES T. P., A. H. BAIRD, D. R. BELLWOOD, M. CARD, S. R. CONNOLLY, C. FOLKE, R. GROSBERG, et al. "Climate change, human impacts, and the resilience of coral reefs." *Science* 301 (2003): 929-33.

HUGHES, T. P., D. R. BELLWOOD, and S. R. CONNOLLY. "Biodiversity hotspots, centers of endemicity, and the conservation of coral reefs." *Ecology Letters* 5 (2002): 775-784.

JACKSON J. B. C., M. X. KIRBY, W. H. BERGER, K.A. BJORNDAL, L W. BOTSFORD, B. J. BOURQUE, R. BRADBURY, et al. "Historical overfishing and the recent collapse of coastal ecosystems." *Science* 293 (2001): 629-38.

LOYA, Y., K SAKAI, K. YAMAZATO, Y. NAKANO, H. SAMBALI, and R. VAN WOESIK. "Coral bleaching: the winners and losers." *Ecology Letters* 4 (2001): 122-131.

MARAGOS, J. E., C. EVANS, and P. HOLTUS. "Reef corals in Kaneohe Bay six years before and after termination of sewage discharges (Oahu, Hawaiian Archipelago). *Proceedings of the fifth international coral reef congress*, Tahiti, 1985. Vol. 4. 189-194.

MARSHALL, P. A., and A. H. BAIRD. "Bleaching of corals on the Great Barrier Reef: differential susceptibilities among taxa." *Coral Reefs* 19 (2000): 155-163.

MUMBY, P. J., C. P. DAHLGREN, A. R. HARBORNE, C. V. KAPPEL, F. MICHELI, D. R. BRUMBAUGH, K. E. HOLMES, et al. "Fishing, trophic cascades, and the process of grazing on coral reefs." *Science* 311 (2006): 98-101.

NYSTRÖM M., C. FOLKE, and F. MOBERG. "Coral reef disturbance and resilience in a human-dominated environment." *Trends in Ecology and Evolution* 15 (2000): 413-417.

PANDOLFI J. M., R. H. BRADBURY, E. SALA, T. P. HUGHES, K. A. BJORNDAL, R. G. COOKE, D. McARDLE, et al. "Global trajectories of the long-term decline of coral reef ecosystems." *Science* 301 (2003): 955-958.

PAULY, D. "Anecdotes and the shifting baseline syndrome of fisheries." *Trends in Ecology and Evolution* 10 (1995): 430.

RUSS, G. R., B. STOCKWELL, and A. C. ALCALA. "Inferring versus measuring rates of recovery in no-take marine reserves." *Marine Ecology Progress Series* 292 (2005): 1-12.

SALE, P. F., R. K. COWEN, B. S. DANILOWICZ, G. P. JONES, J. P. KRITZER, K. C. LINDEMAN, S. PLANES, N. V. C. POLUNIN, et al. "Critical science gaps impede use of no-take fishery reserves." *Trends in Ecology and Evolution* 20 (2005): 74-80.

SCHEFFER M., S. CARPENTER, J. A. FOLEY, C. FOLKE, and B. WALKER. "Catastrophic shifts in ecosystems." *Nature* 413 (2001): 591-596.

WILLIAMSON, D. H., G. R. RUSS, and A. M. AYLING. "No-take marine reserves increase abundance and biomass of reef fish on inshore fringing reefs of the Great Barrier Reef." *Environmental Conservation* 31 (2004): 149-159.

WILKINSON C. R., ed. *Status of the coral reefs of the world: 2008*. Global Coral Reef Monitoring Network and Australian Institute of Marine Science, Townsville, 2008.

LISTS

LIST OF PHOTOGRAPHS

LIST OF ILLUSTRATIONS

INDEX

ABOUT THE AUTHORS

Jennifer Culbertson is research faculty at the University of North Carolina Wilmington (United States). Her work has included an examination of a range of anthropogenic effects in estuarine environments, from oil spills to dredging and sea level rise. Presently, she is examining the effects of increased tidal ranges on sediment biogeochemistry in brackish marshes and tidal freshwater swamps.

e-mail: culbertsonj@uncw.edu

William C. Dennison is Vice President for Science Applications, University of Maryland Center for Environmental Science (United States). He leads the Integration and Application Network, which is a collection of scientists interested in solving, not just studying environmental problems. His interest in environmental problem solving is focused on coastal regions of the world, and Dr. Dennison has conducted research in all of the world's oceans. He has published books and papers on a wide diversity of marine topics, in a spectrum of peer-reviewed scientific journals to more generally accessible science communication products.

e-mail: dennison@umces.edu

Carlos M. Duarte is research professor for the Spanish National Research Council (CSIC) at the Mediterranean Institute for Advanced Studies (IMEDEA) in Esporles (Mallorca, Spain). His work has focused on the ecology and conservation of a range of marine habitats (mangroves, coral reefs, seagrass meadows, algal beds) from the tropics to the poles. He has published over 360 papers on the subject and two books. He currently serves as president of the American Society of Limnology and Oceanography and as editor-in-chief of the journal *Estuaries and Coasts*.

e-mail: carlosduarte@ifisc.uib.es

Robinson (Wally) Fulweiler is assistant professor of earth sciences at Boston University (United States) and a coastal ecosystem ecologist. Her research has included coastal watershed mass balances of major biogenic elements in New England (C, N, P, Si), the biogeochemistry of nitrogen in coastal marine ecosystems, especially sediments, and wetland ecology in coastal Louisiana. Her recent focus has been on how climate change may influence nitrogen fixation and denitrification in estuarine and shelf systems, and anthropogenic impacts on the coastal silica cycle.
e-mail: rwf@acs.bu.edu

Terry Hughes is director of the Australian Research Council (ARC) Centre of Excellence for Coral Reef Studies, at James Cook University (Townsville, Australia). His research focuses on the interaction between people and coral reef ecosystems, particularly in the context of climate change, reef management, and sustainable livelihoods. His field work is based mainly in Australia, the central and western Pacific, and the Caribbean. In 2008, he was awarded the Darwin Medal by the International Society for Reef Studies, for his leading contribution to coral reef science.
e-mail: terry.hughes@jcu.adu.au

Erin L. Kinney is a Ph.D. candidate studying salt marsh and estuarine ecology at the Ecosystems Center, Marine Biological Laboratory (Woods Hole, United States). Erin received a B.A. degree from Dartmouth College and an M.A. from Boston University. Her current activities are focused on understanding the nitrogen sources to Great South Bay, NY, and working with local stakeholders to manage nitrogen loading.
e-mail: ekinney@mbl.edu

Núria Marbà is a scientist for the Spanish National Research Council (CSIC) at the Mediterranean Institute for Advanced Studies (IMEDEA) in Esporles (Mallorca, Spain). Her main research field is the ecology of marine plant populations. She has led and participated in projects on marine ecology, biodiversity, and conservation in European, Australian, Asian, African, and Caribbean coastal regions. Author of around 80 research papers and 2 book chapters, and co-editor of one book, she also sits on the editorial board of the journal *Marine Ecology*.
e-mail: nmarba@imedea.uib-csic.es

Scott Nixon is professor of oceanography and UNESCO/Cousteau Chair in Coastal Ecology at the University of Rhode Island (United States), where he has been on the faculty since 1970. He served for 16 years as director of the Rhode Island Sea Grant College Program and for many years as co-editor-in-chief of *Estuaries and Coasts.* He has published over 100 scientific papers and served on numerous committees of the U.S. National Research Council. He has been recognized with several awards, including the Ketchum Award from the Woods Hole Oceanographic Institution, and the Odum Award from the Estuarine Research Federation.
e-mail: swn@gso.uri.edu

Emily E. Peacock is a research assistant at the Woods Hole Oceanographic Institution (United States). She primarily studies the fate and effects of petroleum hydrocarbons in the marine environment. Her recent Masters work in the Boston University Marine Program examined sediment erosion in relation to long-term petroleum contamination of a New England salt marsh.
e-mail: epeacock@whoi.edu

Stephen Smith is a plant ecologist at the Cape Cod National Seashore (National Park Service, United States) with expertise in plant physiology and plant community ecology. Stephen received a B.S. degree from Florida State University and an M.S and Ph.D. from the University of Miami. His current activities focus on the dynamics of the spatial and temporal variability of plant communities within the different Seashore ecosystems. A large part of this work involves assessments of tidal restoration of salt marshes and ecogeomorphic change.
e-mail: stephen_m_smith@nps.gov

Ivan Valiela has been teaching and doing research since 1969 in Woods Hole (United States) at the Marine Biological Laboratory. He has published over 200 articles on many basic and applied features of coastal environments, and has written *Marine Ecological Processes*, well known as a standard text in marine ecology; *Doing Science*, a guide to design, analysis, and communication of scientific research; and *Global Coastal Change*, a comprehensive overview of the environmental factors changing the marine systems of the world.
e-mail: ivaliela@mbl.edu